Children
of the
Empire

The Extraordinary Lives of
Queen Victoria's Children and
Grandchildren

Michael Farah

Matador
9 Priory Business Park,
Wistow Road, Kibworth Beauchamp,
Leicestershire. LE8 0RX
Tel: 0116 279 2299
Email: books@troubador.co.uk
Web: www.troubador.co.uk/matador
Twitter: @matadorbooks

ISBN 978 1800460 720

British Library Cataloguing in Publication Data.
A catalogue record for this book is available from the British Library.

Printed and bound by CPI Group (UK) Ltd, Croydon, CR0 4YY
Typeset in 11pt Minion Pro by Troubador Publishing Ltd, Leicester, UK

Matador is an imprint of Troubador Publishing Ltd

For my parents, Sam and Esther Farah

Contents

Preface

In "Children of the Empire", I wanted to imagine how the nine children and 38 grandchildren of Queen Victoria and Prince Albert would describe their own lives. How would they have recounted their unique existence and experiences? And how would they have done so to a 21st century audience that remains fascinated by this incredible Royal Family? This book contains the stories of each of them, individually told from a first-person perspective as though they are writing at the end of their lives. Queen Victoria and Prince Albert are generally regarded as having had 42 grandchildren, but four of them were either stillborn or died very shortly after birth, so they have not been included in this book.

Victoria and Albert were keen to marry as many of their children as possible into the other royal houses of Europe in an attempt to ensure peace and prosperity across the continent. The first marriage was arranged for their eldest daughter, Princess Victoria, who was married to Frederick III of Prussia, the future

German Emperor. Queen Victoria also influenced many of her other children and grandchildren's marriages, and eventually they were married into 17 royal houses across Europe, nine of whom became kings or queens. She became known as the Grandmother of Europe.

As I began writing "Children of the Empire", I quickly decided that I wanted to tell their stories through their eyes as if they were recounting them personally. Each account covers the factual events of their personal lives, but I have also expressed their thoughts and feelings where they have been apparent through historical evidence, such as their personal letters. Very little emotion has been added without evidence, except in a few instances where emotions have been attributed to an event that is expected of any normal person.

These personal stories are often tinged with tragedy and sadness, with the loss of loved ones through wars, illness and accidents, and accounts of adultery and loveless marriages, which still resonate with the Royal Family today. There are also uplifting stories of bravery, philanthropy and charitable work. The stories give a fascinating historical insight into the function (and dysfunction) of the Royal Family during and after Queen Victoria's incredible 63-year reign.

Michael Farah

Family Tree of Queen Victoria & Prince Albert

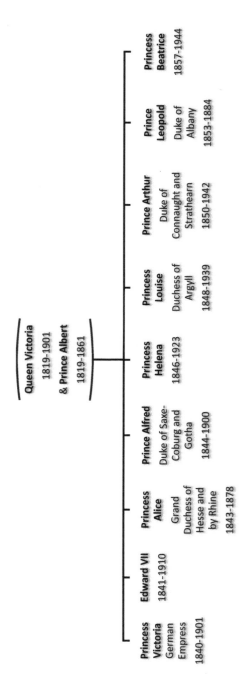

Queen Victoria
1819-1901
& Prince Albert
1819-1861

Princess Victoria
German Empress
1840-1901

Edward VII
1841-1910

Princess Alice
Grand Duchess of Hesse and by Rhine
1843-1878

Prince Alfred
Duke of Saxe-Coburg and Gotha
1844-1900

Princess Helena
1846-1923

Princess Louise
Duchess of Argyll
1848-1939

Prince Arthur
Duke of Connaught and Stratheam
1850-1942

Prince Leopold
Duke of Albany
1853-1884

Princess Beatrice
1857-1944

Family Tree of Princess Victoria

First Child of Queen Victoria

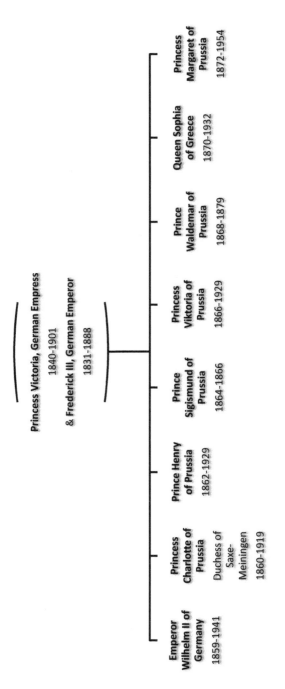

Princess Victoria, German Empress
1840-1901
& Frederick III, German Emperor
1831-1888

Emperor Wilhelm II of Germany
1859-1941

Princess Charlotte of Prussia
Duchess of Saxe-Meiningen
1860-1919

Prince Henry of Prussia
1862-1929

Prince Sigismund of Prussia
1864-1866

Princess Viktoria of Prussia
1866-1929

Prince Waldemar of Prussia
1868-1879

Queen Sophia of Greece
1870-1932

Princess Margaret of Prussia
1872-1954

Princess Victoria

German Empress

Born 21 November 1840 – died 5 August 1901

I am the eldest child of Queen Victoria and Prince Albert. I have four brothers and four sisters. Our main residence was Buckingham Palace but I have a lot of fond memories of Windsor Castle and Balmoral Castle in Scotland, which is where we truly felt like a family. We also went to Osborne House on the Isle of Wight but I prefer Windsor and Balmoral. Like most royal children, I didn't spend that much time with my mother, apart from about an hour a day. I don't remember accompanying her on royal trips but we did go to France on a state visit when I was about 14. I spent a lot of time with my father and had a close relationship with him. Apart from tutoring me, especially in politics, we talked and played games together, like chess, and went for walks. However, most of my education was done by governesses at home.

My brothers all received a better education than the girls. We spoke mainly English at home but we could speak German. My father came from Coburg, a small Duchy in southern Germany,

which I have since visited as an adult. My father didn't have many relatives, just Uncle Ernest, who didn't have any children. My mother has two half siblings but we didn't see them much. There is only a year's age gap between me and my brother Bertie, who later became Edward VII, although there is obviously a large age gap of 17 years between me and my youngest sister, Beatrice.

I married Prince Frederick of Prussia (the largest state of modern Germany) when I was just 17. It was arranged by my parents as they hoped that by marrying me to the future King of Prussia, our two countries would become closer via family ties. I called him Fritz. We first met when he visited England in 1851 for the Great Exhibition, an international exhibition of industrial technology and design in London. I showed him around – his English was not very good so we conversed in German. We met a few times after that and we had a courtship, so I knew him more or less by the time we were married. I was happy to marry him because I wanted to do my duty for my country and I had already grown fond of him.

We married in the Chapel Royal at St James' Palace. We had a short honeymoon in Windsor and then we went to Prussia. It was difficult there – I found it difficult to adapt to a different culture, different court culture and different attitudes. I didn't get on with my in-laws or with most of the Prussian aristocracy due to our differences in values, they being very conservative, whereas I am liberal.

We had eight children, born fairly close together. I had my first child, Wilhelm, when I was 18 and it was a very difficult birth. The doctors gave me too much chloroform during the labour, which meant that I was unable to play an active role. I thought the baby and I were going to die, but after 51 hours the doctors managed to deliver him. Wilhelm suffered a withered left arm. This left me feeling very guilty and I think it has affected him, especially his confidence. I know it wasn't my fault but I still feel bad. I was very young and inexperienced when I had him. I let myself be influenced by others, which I now regret, such as not playing more of an active role in his formative years. I have always had very different political opinions from Wilhelm. I don't get on with him very well and have always had an easier relationship with my younger children, which Wilhelm resents.

The other births were all much easier but two of my children died in childhood. Sigismund died of meningitis and Waldemar died of diphtheria. The deaths of my two sons hit me very hard. With the exception of my husband, who shared my pain; I did not find anyone else to be particularly sympathetic. When Sigismund died, I wrote to my mother of my heartbreak, but she didn't seem to understand my pain; at that point she had not lost any of her children and she was still deeply grieving the death of my father, thus she responded that losing a husband is far worse than losing a child.

Sadly, my beloved father died in 1861. I rushed straight to England for the funeral. I was devastated, as I was so close to him and he was only 42.

I opened a college, the Victoria Lyceum in Berlin, to prepare girls for university, to bring them up to the same standard as boys. I am a firm believer in education for girls as well as boys. I also have championed women's rights, including their right to vote. We haven't won that right yet but I hope it will happen one day, although perhaps not in my lifetime. I have also spoken out against anti-Semitism and my husband and I visited Jewish synagogues to show our support. There is a lot of anti-Semitism in Germany, far more than in England.

In 1862, there was a constitutional crisis in Prussia. My father-in-law clashed with the Prussian parliament over proposed reforms to the Army. The situation between the King and the parliament became so bad that my father-in-law considered abdicating, which would of course have made my husband king. Although I tried to persuade my husband to accept his father's abdication, he refused to accept it as he did not want to fail in his duties as a son. In the end, my father-in-law didn't abdicate as it was then that he appointed Otto von Bismarck prime minister, a staunch conservative who ruled with an iron fist and greatly reduced the importance of parliament.

Whenever I think of Bismarck I feel so angry. I think of all I tried to achieve in Germany by working with my husband to make it more liberal and how Bismarck ruined my hopes and dreams by ensuring it would never happen, by manipulating Wilhelm and turning him against us, his own parents, destroying all influence we had with him and ruining our relationship with him.

One of the most difficult times in my life was the Austrian-Prussian War in 1866, when Alice, my sister, and I found that we were enemies as our husbands were fighting against each other. Fortunately, the war was quickly resolved.

I was very much in love with my husband – we had a good marriage of about 30 years. Sadly, I was widowed at the age of 48 when Fritz died of cancer. He was only Emperor for 99 days after his father died. Wilhelm succeeded his father. I disagree with some of his policies. I think his rule is oppressive and reactionary; he is currently in an arms race with Britain. I'm concerned with where it might lead. Obviously, my mother was Queen in England until a few short months ago. She only visited me twice since I was married, but I travelled back to England many times to see her and my siblings. My mother sent me literally thousands of letters. I found her overbearing but being in different countries, I think I found her easier to deal with my than my siblings.

In my younger days, I had hopes that when Fritz became German Emperor, we would be able to transform Germany into a more liberal society but unfortunately, as Fritz died after only 99 days, that did not happen. It won't happen now that Wilhelm is Emperor, as he is far more conservative. After my husband's death, I retired from political life but still maintain an active public life. I didn't want to withdraw like my mother did after my father died and I knew that Fritz would want me to continue leading a full life.

My children all married other royalty. They all live here, except for my daughter Sophia, as she married the Crown Prince of Greece. I have many grandchildren but unfortunately I don't see Wilhelm's children very much as I don't get on with my daughter-in-law, Augusta Victoria, very well. She is very conservative and doesn't like any new ideas. In that way, she and Wilhelm are perfect for each other.

I have been ill now for about three years and know that the doctors cannot help me.

Postscript: Victoria died of cancer on 5 August 1901, aged 60 seven months after the death of her mother, Queen Victoria. She was buried in the royal mausoleum in Potsdam, next to her husband and their two sons who had died in childhood.

Emperor Wilhelm II
of Germany

Born 27 January 1859 – died 4 June 1941

At the time of my birth, my father Frederick was second in line to the Prussian throne after my grandfather Wilhelm, who was serving as Prince Regent of Prussia for his elder brother who had suffered a stroke, King Frederick William IV of Prussia. King Frederick died in 1861, at which point my grandfather became King of Prussia. My mother was Princess Victoria, the eldest child of Queen Victoria.

My mother had a difficult birth. She was in labour for 52 hours and was given too much chloroform, which meant that she couldn't push, so the doctor had to pull me out. This resulted in me having a withered left arm, which was about six inches shorter than my right arm, a condition known as Erb's palsy. I couldn't use my left arm, so it meant that some things, like cutting up food, were very difficult to do. Riding a horse was also difficult because it requires a lot of balance, which is usually accomplished by using your arms.

As a child, I was forced to undergo some really unpleasant

treatments and none of them worked. I was given electro-therapy, which was painful. One really disgusting treatment was having a dead hare wrapped around my arm. When I think back to the 19th century, medical treatments were quite superstitious at times. I am surprised my mother allowed it but I suppose she was quite desperate to help me. These treatments went on for quite a while before they eventually gave up and realised that nothing was helping me.

I had five other surviving siblings and two brothers who died young. I didn't really have a good relationship with my mother, partly because I always felt that she favoured my other brothers and sisters over me, particularly my three younger sisters. I got on better with my father – when I was young I looked up to him as a war hero. He fought in many wars, particularly the Franco-Prussian War, which ultimately led to the unification of Germany. I was home educated at first but later my brother Henry and I went off to boarding school. We spoke German and English because of my parents but were also taught French, as all royals should speak French.

On my 18th birthday I was invested with the Order of the Garter by my grandmother Queen Victoria which was a huge honour because it was Britain's highest honour. I then went to the University of Bonn for four terms, where I studied politics and law. While I was at university I fell passionately in love with my cousin, Princess Elisabeth of Hesse, but unfortunately she did not feel the same about me. I was hugely disappointed, but in time my feelings for her subsided. After university, I joined the military but because of my arm I couldn't fight so I mainly had to make do with ceremonial duties.

I married Augusta Victoria, a German Princess, in 1881. We had seven children: six sons and one daughter. My wife was fairly introverted and preferred to stay at the palace most of the time, so she rarely accompanied me on my duties. We divided our time between Berlin and Potsdam. We had a happy marriage and family life.

In 1871 the German Empire was formed and my grandfather became the first Emperor. My father became Emperor in 1888 when I was only 29 but he was already ill with throat cancer and he died only 99 days into his reign. My mother always insisted on getting English doctors and it was an English doctor who caused my withered arm and an English doctor who murdered my father through complete incompetence. So after my father died, I ascended the throne. My mother then became the Dowager Empress and lived quietly in retirement. She still played a role with her charitable works but she didn't have a public role.

My relationship with my mother improved somewhat after I became Emperor. Although I got on well with my father as a child, our relationship became more strained as an adult because we had different political views; mine were more conservative. As Emperor, I was head of the Lutheran Church in Germany. My reign overlapped three British monarchs; first, my grandmother, Queen Victoria; followed by my uncle Bertie, who became Edward VII; and then my cousin, George V. I had a very close relationship with my grandmother, Queen Victoria, and in fact she died in my arms when I was visiting her at Osborne House. I am not sure if I was her favourite grandchild but I was the eldest one, so I think I had a special place in her heart.

I had many responsibilities as the Emperor and I shared power with the Reichstag (German parliament). Germany had a close relationship with the Austrian-Hungarian Empire and also with the Ottoman Empire, both of which were our allies in the Great War. We had a poorer relationship with Russia, France and Britain, all of which we eventually fought against in the war.

Germany had an arms race with Britain, during which both countries built up their Navies. I found Britain to be very antagonistic and it continued to increase its already large Empire through the scramble for Africa. In 1896, Britain was not very happy when I sent a telegraph to Paul Kruger, President of the Transvaal (a state located in modern South Africa), congratulating him on his success in defeating the British. In 1908 I gave an interview to the Daily Telegraph newspaper suggesting that a large proportion of the German population was anti-English, which was true, but obviously that didn't go down very well in England.

Although my relatives were in power in both Britain and Russia (Tsarina Alexandra of Russia was my cousin and I was also more distantly related to her husband, Tsar Nicholas II), that didn't stop me going to war against them – obviously I had to put my country first. However, I was surprised when my cousin, George V, did not offer asylum to his cousin Tsar Nicholas and his family during the Russian Revolution, which could possibly have saved them from their executions in Russia. I did try to save them later, when I made peace with Russia, but by then it was too late, as the Bolshevik government was reluctant to release them. I was obviously shocked and saddened by their executions.

At the end of the Great War in 1918, the German people were starving and many disturbances broke out. This escalated and the military mutinied, which shocked me as I had never thought the military would become disloyal to me. Eventually, my position became untenable, so I was forced to abdicate, along with the other German monarchs. A new order and democratic form of government was then established. Prince Max of Baden became the transitional Chancellor (Prime Minister) until Frederick Ebert became the first President of the new republic. I accepted my fate but I was worried about Germany's long-term prospects. However, I recognised that I needed to give up power. After all,

I did not want to end up being executed like Tsar Nicholas in Russia. We then went into exile in the Netherlands, where I was offered asylum. Apart from my immediate family, the other German monarchs were allowed to stay in Germany, although they had to give up their titles and live as private citizens.

In the Netherlands, we purchased a country house and I have lived here ever since. I have published my memoirs and live quietly in retirement. I enjoy hunting and have developed an interest in archaeology and I also learned Dutch. Six of my seven children are still alive but sadly my youngest son, Prince Joachim, committed suicide in 1920 by shooting himself, at the age of 29. I was never really sure what drove him to do that but can only guess that he couldn't cope with the new reality of no longer being royal and living in exile, as well as his recent divorce.

Unfortunately, my wife died in 1921. I think she may have died of a broken heart after Joachim committed suicide. However, I quickly found love again and I remarried in 1922, to the former Princess Hermine. I probably wouldn't have been able to marry her had I still been Emperor because no doubt people would have thought she was beneath me in station, but as I was in exile I could do what I liked. Hermine was 35 and I was 63.

Fortunately, I was allowed to keep our property, so we have been able to live comfortably here, which also means my children have not had to work. My children are able to visit Germany and keep an eye on our estates, from which we derive an income. I am ashamed to admit that one of my sons, August Wilhelm, has become an active Nazi. He joined the Nazi Party and allowed himself to be used in propaganda, campaigning for the Nazis to gain votes in elections and by accompanying Adolf Hitler.

Postscript: Wilhelm II died in 1941 of pulmonary embolus, aged 82, and he was buried in the Netherlands. After the Second World War, August Wilhelm was arrested by the USA and put on trial and found guilty of being a high ranking Nazi. He was a stormtrooper (SA) as well as representing the Nazi Party in the Reichstag. He was sentenced to two-and-a-half years' forced labour, although since he had already been imprisoned in an internal camp for that long, he did not have to serve his sentence. Wilhelm's eldest son, Crown Prince Wilhelm, also became close to the Nazis and he was captured by the French after the war and interned as a war criminal. He lived under house arrest until his death in 1951.

Princess Charlotte
of Prussia, Duchess of Saxe-Meiningen
Born 24 July 1860 – died 1 Oct 1919

I am the second child of Emperor Frederick and Empress Victoria of Germany, although at the time of my birth they were Prince and Princess of Prussia and my grandfather was regent for his brother King Frederick Wilhelm IV of Prussia. Unlike my brother Wilhelm, my birth was straightforward. I had a conventional childhood for royalty and was educated at home. However, my mother said I was a difficult child, an indifferent student and that I have a somewhat nervous disposition. My relationship with her was strained because of the differences between our personalities. She placed great emphasis on education but I was not very academic.

We spent the winters in Berlin and the summers in Potsdam. We visited England every year, so I got to know my English cousins as well as my German family. As a child, I had a very close relationship with my paternal grandparents, Emperor Wilhelm I and Empress Augusta, along with Wilhelm and Henry, my brothers closest in age. My younger siblings, Victoria, Sophia

and Margaret, were closer to our maternal grandmother, Queen Victoria. I am not really sure why that was, although there was an age gap between Wilhelm, myself and Henry and the three younger siblings because we had two brothers in between, Sigismund and Waldemar, who both died in childhood. Sigismund was a year old when he died and I was only six, so I don't remember him too well, but Waldemar died when he was eleven and I was nineteen. He died of diphtheria only four months after my aunt Alice and cousin Marie also died from the illness, so that was a sad time for our family.

I married my second cousin, Prince Bernard of Saxe-Meiningen, heir to the Duchy of Saxe-Meiningen, when I was only 16. We married for love but later we grew apart. He was devoted to the Army and I had other interests. I very much enjoyed a good social life. We had one child, Feodora. I really disliked being pregnant – I found it very restrictive – so after I had Feodora I decided I did not want any more children. My mother was very disappointed about that and couldn't understand my decision, as she had eight children and her mother had nine. Most women had many children at the time, so I was very unusual.

In 1891, a scandal hit Berlin society because over a four-year period hundreds of anonymous letters were sent to prominent members of the court, including Wilhelm and his wife. The letters were all written in the same handwriting and they included scandalous gossip and accusations, while some even contained pornographic images. Wilhelm ordered an investigation but the writer or writers were never discovered. Some people thought it was me because I did have a reputation for having a sharp tongue and loving a bit of gossip, but of course it wasn't. Others thought it might have been the Empress' brother in collaboration with his mistress, but again it was not proven. No-one is really sure why these letters were sent – there was no suggestion of blackmail, rather it seemed that it was more to do with causing embarrassment. The letter writer seemed to have a great deal of knowledge of the Royal Family, so it was likely that it was either a family member or someone very close.

During this time I lost my diary, in which I had recorded some secrets. Eventually the diary was found and handed to Wilhelm – I'm not sure that he ever forgave me for some of the comments I had made. It is entirely possible that someone had taken my diary and used it to write the letters, so I was blamed anyway.

I used to have a close relationship with Wilhelm but we grew apart after he got married as I didn't get along with his wife (our mutual dislike for Wilhelm's wife was one of the few things my mother and I had in common). After the letters scandal, our relationship got even worse. As a result, my husband was transferred to a regiment in the quiet town of Treslaw, so we were basically exiled from the Berlin court for a good few months.

A few years later in 1896, my sister-in-law, the Empress, accused me of having an affair. Fortunately, my husband believed that it was not true and he defended me. My husband almost had to leave the Army, but the man I was accused of having an affair with returned to court with his wife and the situation was resolved. Many believed that this accusation damaged the reputation of the monarchy.

I have a difficult relationship with Feodora, my daughter. I think we are too alike and we seem to clash. She married a man 15 years older than her, who was not wealthy or high-ranking, and I didn't particularly like him. I admit that I was not that happy about it initially, but I came round eventually. He seemed unable to control Feodora, who is very strong-willed. Feodora can't have children, so I don't have any grandchildren. She has had operations to try to help her have children but they have been unsuccessful. It is sad for her as she obviously wanted children. We have been estranged for a while but I finally wrote to her again after I heard she had undergone a dangerous operation to help her conceive. I was outraged that such a difficult operation had been approved and I went to visit her in hospital.

I have a few health problems – I suffer with rheumatism, joint pain, headaches, insomnia, indigestion and other things. I have had these problems all my adult life and they have gradually become worse and sometimes are really bad. The doctors don't seem to know what causes these problems. In 1911, when I was attending George V's coronation, the weather was so hot that it left me bedridden for a time with pain in my limbs. My mother had some minor health complaints too, like headaches and skin rashes, but my problems seem much worse. Feodora also has similar health complaints to me, so it seems it is something that runs in our family.

In 1914 my husband succeeded his father to become the Duke of Saxe-Meiningen and he ruled until the Revolution in 1918. He was away for most of that time, fighting in the Great War, and I was left behind overseeing the Duchy, where I mainly served as a figurehead. In 1918 my husband was forced to abdicate, along with all the other German royals. Fortunately, we were able to stay in Germany – it was only Wilhelm as the former Emperor who had to leave with his family. We had to give up our titles but the new German government allowed us to keep our territorial designations as surnames, so now I am known as Charlotte von Saxe-Meiningen, which has taken some adjusting. Luckily, we have kept all our property. We have lost some income but most of our money is generated from the estate. The situation has probably affected my husband more than me because obviously he is no longer a ruling Duke or in the Army.

During the war, my health got worse and I had to take opium to help with the pain. After the war was over I travelled to Baden to seek medical treatment for my heart.

Postscript: Charlotte died in 1919 of a heart attack, aged 59. It is believed that Charlotte and Feodora suffered from porphyria, a genetic blood disorder which would account for her many ailments, including turning her urine dark red. It has also affected a number of members of the British Royal Family. George III was the most famous sufferer and the disease was responsible for his insanity. For Charlotte, the symptoms were not as severe, but would have accounted for her hyperactivity, mood swings and nervous disposition. As a young girl she was seen to be agitated and used to pull at her clothes. Her mother reported to Queen Victoria that she was nervous and sensitive, her sleep was not very sound and she was very thin. The symptoms are known to increase with age. Porphyria in the British Royal Family has been traced all the way back to Mary Queen of Scots and has most recently been seen in Prince William of Gloucester who died in 1972.

Prince Henry

of Prussia

Born 14 August 1862 – died 20 April 1929

I am the third child of Emperor Frederick of Germany and Empress Victoria. I had a conventional childhood and was initially educated at home with my older brother Wilhelm. Later we were sent off to school and at 15 years of age enrolled in the Imperial Cadet Programme with the Navy. There was more pressure on Wilhelm as he was heir to the throne but things were easier for me. I was close to my parents and paternal grandparents in Germany. My maternal grandfather, Prince Albert, died just before I was born but I also had a good relationship with Queen Victoria, my maternal grandmother. At the time of my birth, my father was the Crown Prince of Prussia but he became the Emperor of Germany in 1888 when I was 26. He died in the same year and then Wilhelm became Emperor.

Also that year, I fell in love and married Princess Irene of Hesse and by Rhine, my first cousin. Although we had seen each other as children, we didn't really know each other that well because I lived in Prussia and she lived in Darmstadt, which

are some distance from each other in Germany. Fortunately, my father was able to attend our wedding before he died. We had three sons: Waldemar, Sigismund and Henry. Very sadly, Henry died when he was only four years old. He was a haemophiliac and he bumped his head, which resulted in his tragically early death. I don't think Irene was ever the same again.

I have spent a lot of my adult life serving in the German Imperial Navy as an officer which means I was away from home quite a lot. However, when I was home I carried out some royal engagements. I have travelled to many places, including America in 1902 as the royal representative, where I met politicians and dignitaries. I think I made a good impression, even though at the time Germany was not on great terms with the USA. I served in the Great War as Commander-in-Chief of the Baltic fleet. Although Germany lost the war, I consider that I was successful as Commander-in-Chief. The Baltic fleet fought against Russian ships. However, it was difficult when we lost our sailors because I took my position very seriously and I cared about my men.

My relationship with Wilhelm has been strained for most of our lives as he seems to resent me. He thinks people like me more than him, which is possibly true as he seems to have a habit of getting on the wrong side of people. I believe that my brother was a good Emperor but I don't think he was a good war leader, which I find somewhat ironic as he appeared to want to go to war. I have never understood why he was so desperate for war. I found my brother's abdication at the end of the war quite shocking, but in hindsight it probably wasn't that surprising. As I was considered a minor royal by then, I was allowed to stay in Germany but we moved from Berlin to the north of the country. I left the Navy but as I was nearing retirement anyway it wasn't too difficult for me, although I still love the sea and go yachting when I can. I also love motor cars.

After the war, we received news that my wife's relatives in Russia had been murdered by the Bolsheviks. Two of her sisters, Ella and Alix, had married into the Russian Imperial Family. Alix married Tsar Nicholas II and they and their five children were all murdered. Afterwards some imposters started appearing, including one claiming to be her niece, Anastasia. Irene went to visit but she didn't believe that it was her. However, this upset her so much that in the end I forbade any mention of the imposters in Irene's presence. Ella was also murdered by the Bolsheviks.

My son Sigismund left Germany in 1927 for Costa Rica, where he now works in coffee planting. Obviously, he wouldn't have done that had he still been a prince, but life has changed for us all. Waldemar is a haemophiliac, so he could not serve in the military. He has to be very careful about what he does because of his condition, as even a minor injury can cause death.

I am 66 now and I have throat cancer, like my father before me. I am sad, not for myself but for Irene, because she is sensitive and fragile and I hope she copes without me.

Postscript: Henry died on 20 April 1929, aged 66.

Prince Sigismund

of Prussia

Born 15 September 1864 – died 18 June 1866

Postscript: *Prince Sigismund of Prussia was the fourth child of Emperor Frederick of Germany and Empress Victoria. He died of diphtheria before reaching his second birthday. Prussia was at war at that time and most doctors were serving at the front, so there was a lack of medical care. He was the first grandchild of Queen Victoria to die. His mother, Victoria, wrote to her mother, Queen Victoria, expressing her heartbreak, but the Queen responded by saying that "losing a husband is far worse than losing a child".*

Princess Viktoria
of Prussia

Born 12 April 1866 – died 13 November 1929

I am the fifth child of Emperor Frederick and Empress Victoria. Growing up, I was closest to my sisters, Sophia and Margaret. I was also close to my maternal grandmother, Queen Victoria, but not so close to my paternal grandparents, who seemed to give more attention to my older siblings, probably because they favoured their grandsons.

In 1881 I fell in love when I was only fifteen with Prince Alexander of Battenberg. He was the brother-in-law of my aunt, Princess Beatrice. Prince Alexander had become the ruling Prince of Bulgaria in 1879, when Bulgaria became independent from the Ottoman Empire. Unfortunately, we weren't allowed to marry because although my parents and Queen Victoria were happy with the match, my paternal grandfather, Emperor Wilhelm I, and the Chancellor, Otto von Bismarck, were against us marrying for political reasons. At that time, Germany and Russia were allies, but Russia was not on good terms with Bulgaria. I was heartbroken that we were not allowed to marry.

Later, when I was 24, I married Prince Adolf, who was from a small state in Germany, Schamburg-Lippe. We cared for each other but I can't say we were ever truly in love. We were unable to have children. I had a miscarriage early in the marriage, after which I had no more children, which was very sad.

I helped my husband with his royal duties as he was the Regent Prince of Schamburg-Lippe for his brother, Prince Alexander, who was unable to carry out his duties due to a mental illness. Adolf died in 1916 at the age of 56 after an illness. After his death, I moved back to Prussia. Shortly afterwards, the Great War ended and all the German monarchies were abolished. I hoped that after the war we could all be friends with our British relatives but George V, my cousin, said that he didn't think that would be possible for a number of years.

In 1927 I married for a second time to Alexander Zoubkoff, a Russian refugee in Germany. He was 35 years younger than me. My brothers and sisters did not approve of the marriage. I had high hopes for the marriage but have been sorely disappointed. My finances were in a precarious state and he has squandered the little money I have left. I have had to call in the receivers and sell some of my things at a palace auction to pay off my debts. Unfortunately, it did not raise much money and I still have a lot of debts. I have now moved to a much smaller property and I am in the process of divorcing him.

Postscripts: A few days after announcing her intention to divorce, Viktoria died of pneumonia, aged 63. The divorce petition was on the grounds that Alexander was being expelled from Germany because of his behaviour, that he had been unable to maintain her and that conjugal relations did not exist.

Prince Waldemar

of Prussia

Born 10 February 1868 – died 27 March 1879

Postscipt: *Prince Waldemar was the sixth child of Emperor Frederick and Empress Victoria of Germany. He was described as a lively, spirited child who was quick to learn. He loved animals and even had a pet crocodile. By the time he reached school age, his mother decided to teach her younger children herself, as she was dissatisfied with the way the older siblings had turned out. Some people thought that he was her favourite.*

In 1878 Waldemar's mother, Victoria, went to visit Princess Alice, her sister, in Darmstadt. Most of Alice's family were ill with diphtheria and Alice and her baby daughter, Marie, died a short time later. Although Victoria did not contract the illness, Waldemar then became ill. He died from diphtheria at the age of 11 and was buried next to his brother, Sigismund, in Potsdam. Their parents were later laid to rest in the same place.

Queen Sophia

of Greece

Born 14 June 1870 – died 13 January 1932

I am the seventh child of Emperor Frederick and Empress Victoria of Germany. I had a happy childhood and was educated at home with the siblings closest in age to me – Waldemar, Margaret and Victoria. Waldemar died when I was only eight, which was very sad but had the effect of drawing my sisters Margaret and Victoria and me closer to our mother. We grew up isolated from the Berlin Court because my parents were not on good terms with my paternal grandparents, but we did make frequent visits to see my maternal grandmother, Queen Victoria, in England. I was 18 when my father became the Emperor and my status rose briefly but did not last long, as he died after only 99 days in power, and then my brother Wilhelm became the Emperor.

In 1887 I fell in love with Crown Prince Constantine of Greece while I was at the Golden Jubilee celebrations of Queen Victoria. It was a huge event and there were many foreign royals there. Tino, as I call him, was only a couple of years older than

me. Both my mother and Queen Victoria approved of him, although I think my mother found it hard to think that I might move to a faraway country. Tino then came to Berlin to attend my father's funeral and we were engaged in September 1888. Most of my family were happy about our relationship, except for my brother Wilhelm and his wife, and Tino's mother, Queen Olga, who was not too happy because I was not Greek Orthodox. Nevertheless, we married in Athens in October 1889. The wedding was attended by my mother and my siblings as well as Uncle Bertie, Aunt Alix (the Prince and Princess of Wales) and my English cousins. I became the Crown Princess of Greece. The Greek people were very happy with our marriage because legend said that when King Constantine and Queen Sophia ascended the throne, Constantinople would fall into Greek hands.

Life in Greece was very different from what I was used to. Everything seemed smaller and more down to earth. We led a relatively simple life, which I liked, and I learned Greek. We had six children. After I had my first child, a son, I converted to Greek Orthodoxy and my mother-in-law, the Queen, was delighted, as were the Greek people. My mother adored the grandchildren.

I returned to Germany for my sister Viktoria's wedding and told my brother Wilhelm about my religious conversion, but he was very angry. I had a very heated argument with his wife, who told me I would go to hell. Shortly after, my sister-in-law went into premature labour, for which my brother blamed me for upsetting her. Wilhelm threatened to exclude me from the

Prussian Royal Family. I wrote a letter to them explaining the reasons for my conversion but he was not understanding at all and he forbade me from returning to Germany for three years. However, I ignored that and visited anyway, but our relationship was strained.

Back in Greece, I followed the example of my mother-in-law and got involved with social work with the underprivileged by promoting education, hospitals, orphanages and soup kitchens and helping refugees from the Ottoman Empire. I worked with the Greek Red Cross, helping wounded soldiers by founding field hospitals.

Tino and I were happy in the first years of marriage but as time went on he started having extra-marital affairs. I tried to follow the example of my mother-in-law and not let it bother me, but we drifted apart over time.

In 1913, my father-in-law was assassinated at the age of 67 when he was out for his afternoon walk. He was shot by someone belonging to a socialist organisation. He had been approaching his 50th anniversary on the throne and was considering abdicating in favour of Tino, but sadly this happened before he could do that. So Constantine ascended the throne and I became Queen. He reigned throughout the Great War. The political situation was very difficult. We tried to stay neutral but were accused of being pro-German and we clashed with the Greek Prime Minister. In 1917 Tino was forced to abdicate and we went to Switzerland with our eldest son, George. Our financial position was precarious and Tino became depressed. My mother-in-law had already returned to Russia. George married Princess Elisabeth of Romania and my daughter Helen married the Crown Prince of Romania. I was happy about George's marriage but I didn't approve of Helen's husband, as he didn't have a very good reputation. He was a known womaniser and sadly their marriage broke down.

Our second son, Alexander, became King as the Greek

people did not want George to be King either, but I think he was more of a puppet monarch. I never saw him again because I was never allowed to go back to Greece. Alexander fell in love with a commoner called Aspasia, whom he married, but it was such a scandal for a member of the Royal Family to marry someone who wasn't royal. Still worse was to come, because in 1920, Alexander died from sepsis following a freak accident. He was bitten by a monkey when out walking his dog. The monkey attacked his dog and when he tried to separate them he was bitten. This is possibly the worst thing that has ever happened to me. I was not even allowed to visit him as he lay dying. My mother-in-law travelled back to Greece to be by his side but sadly he died before she arrived.

After Alexander died, Queen Olga became Queen Regent of Greece while the Greeks figured out what they wanted. They offered the throne to my third son, Pavlos, but he refused without a referendum. Eventually, Tino was reinstated on the throne, which was quite a turnaround. In 1921 Aspasia gave birth to Alexander's posthumous child, a girl she named Alexandra. She was my first grandchild and she helped me to recover from the death of my son. We welcomed them into the Royal Family and they were made princesses.

However, just when we thought things were looking up, everything went wrong again. In 1922 Tino had to abdicate again, following a war Greece had with Turkey. We had to go into exile but this time we went to Italy. Tino was very depressed again and sometimes spent hours just staring into space. I was very worried about him and he died in 1923 of a brain haemorrhage. The Greek government refused to allow his remains to be buried in Greece. They even stripped us of our Greek nationality but fortunately, as the Greek Royal Family are an offshoot of the Danish Royal Family, we were given Danish nationality. I lived in Italy with my daughters Irene and Katherine, and we were joined there by Aspasia and Alexandra. Later on, Helen came to live with us following the breakdown of her marriage. During the summer holidays, her son Michael visited us. I have no wish to live in Germany but I do go there to visit my sister Margaret.

My eldest son George became King but he had to abdicate in 1924 when Greece became a republic and he went to live in Romania, his wife's country. I believe that Greece will one day restore the monarchy again.

After all the difficulties I had with my brother Wilhelm, I finally went to visit him in the Netherlands for his 70th birthday. I hadn't seen him since 1914.

Postscript: Sophia contracted cancer and went to Frankfurt to be treated. She died in the New Year of 1932, surrounded by her children, aged 61. She was buried in Florence, Italy. In 1935 the monarchy was restored in Greece and George II became King again. In 1940 Germany invaded Greece and the Royal Family had to go into exile for the duration of the war. After the war they returned to Greece, but George died soon after. He was succeeded by his brother Pavlos, who reigned until his death in 1964. He was succeeded by his son, Constantine II. In 1967 there was a military coup and Greece again became a republic.

Princess Margaret

of Prussia

Born 22 April 1872 – died 22 January 1954

I am the youngest and eighth child of Emperor Frederick and Empress Victoria of Germany. At the time of my birth, my parents were the Crown Prince and Princess of Prussia and the German Empire. My nickname was Mossy and my sister Sophia's nickname was Sossy. At the time of my christening, I had some hair which I'm told looked like moss, hence my nickname. I had a close relationship with my parents, especially my mother, and with my sisters, Moretta (Viktoria) and Sossy (Sophia).

I fell in love with Prince Maximilian of Baden but he wasn't interested in me. Later, I fell in love with Prince Frederick Karl of Hesse and we married on 25 January 1893, when I was 21. We were second cousins as we were both great-grandchildren of King Frederick Wilhelm III of Prussia. Initially, my brother Wilhelm opposed the match because he thought Frederick was beneath me but eventually he relented and gave his blessing. Our marriage was very happy. We had six sons and led a fairly quiet life. I think Frederick was my mother's favourite son-in-law.

In 1918 Frederick accepted the throne of the newly independent Finland but then after the end of the war, he was forced to renounce it as the Allies would not have accepted a former German monarch taking a throne in Europe. Germany became a republic in 1918 so we lost our royal

Princess Margaret with her husband, Prince Frederick Karl

titles and we became private citizens. Life didn't change too much for us. We kept our estate and my inheritance from my mother.

My early life was very privileged but things got worse and worse during the two world wars. I have suffered one tragedy after another. My two eldest sons were killed in action in the First World War. Frederick Wilhelm was 23 and Maximilian was only 20 and their deaths were heart-breaking. Philip, Christoph and Wolfgang all joined the Nazi Party in the 1930s. Philip and Wolfgang joined the Stormtroopers, a paramilitary group which provided protection at Nazi rallies and disrupted meetings of opposing parties. Philip rose to be a high-ranking Nazi and served as a go-between for German Nazis and Italian Fascists, but he eventually fell out of favour and he and his wife Mafalda, an Italian Princess, were sent to a concentration camp. Fortunately, their four children were kept safe in the Vatican.

Mafalda was killed but Philip survived the Second World War after being in solitary confinement for two years. After the war he was then imprisoned by the Allies and was finally released in 1947. Christoph was a Commander of the Air Reserves and joined the SS but he became disenchanted with the Nazi Party and he was killed in a plane crash in 1943. Wolfgang's wife was also killed in an air raid. I also lost my husband, Frederick, in 1940 at the age of 72. My only consolation during the war was that I had my grandchildren with me. After the Second World War, our family jewels that were worth around £2 million were stolen and although the thieves were eventually caught, they only managed to recover a very small portion of the jewels.

Postscript: Margaret died in 1954, in Kronberg, Germany, aged 81.

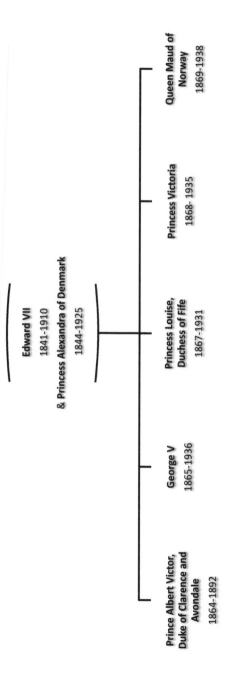

Family Tree of Edward VII

Second Child of Queen Victoria

Edward VII
1841-1910
& Princess Alexandra of Denmark
1844-1925

Prince Albert Victor, Duke of Clarence and Avondale
1864-1892

George V
1865-1936

Princess Louise, Duchess of Fife
1867-1931

Princess Victoria
1868- 1935

Queen Maud of Norway
1869-1938

King Edward VII

Born 9 November 1841–died 6 May 1910

I am Albert Edward, first son of Queen Victoria and Prince Albert. I never really liked my name Albert, so to my family and friends I was known as Bertie. When I became King, in 1901, I chose for myself the name Edward.

I had a bit of a miserable childhood. My parents, especially my father, pushed me very hard. I suppose they wanted to prepare me to be the perfect monarch. But surely no one can be 'perfect'. The pressure they put on me only served to cause me a huge amount of stress.

I had a very protected childhood in the royal residences and, like all my siblings, was home educated. Some limited independence came later, when I went to the University of Oxford, where I finally made a few friends. As a future monarch, I also needed to get some military experience, so after Oxford I went into the Army, which I enjoyed. Throughout all this, I still had duties to fulfil as heir to the throne and Prince of Wales,

which lasted until I finally ascended the throne in 1901, when I was 59.

The relationship with my parents was difficult, to say the least. My father was physically present but emotionally distant and difficult. My mother blamed me for my father's death. I was twenty and having an affair with a woman with whom they did not approve. She said that if my personal life hadn't caused my father so much stress he would never have gone for a walk in such foul weather and consequently not have died, but I think she was being a bit silly about that. In reality, the doctors said he died of typhoid fever.

My mother was also very controlling and she arranged my marriage to Princess Alexandra of Denmark. Alix (her nickname) and I were never really in love. How could we be? Mama never gave us space or left us in peace, even though we didn't live in the same palace with her. Some people think that all six of our children were born prematurely but that wasn't actually true. Alix just gave my mother false due dates so that she could have the children without her being there.

Alix did give birth to a boy who only lived for a day, but all our other children survived into adulthood. However, my eldest child and heir to the throne, Eddy (Albert Victor, Duke of Clarence and Avondale), died tragically of pneumonia in his early 20s just when he was about to get married. Now that burden falls to George, my second son. I believe George will make a good King. George married Eddy's fiancée, and she will be a great support to him when he becomes King.

Some people say I have led a hedonistic lifestyle. In truth, I did enjoy visiting Paris and being entertained by certain ladies of the night. I also had a few mistresses in my time, some long-term. And yes I slept with married women; but that wasn't so unusual for someone in my position.

For 12 years, Alice Keppel has been my favourite mistress. She just makes me happy and is one of the few people who can cheer me up when I am a bit cranky. Alice is in fact married to someone else but that doesn't interfere with our relationship. Aristocratic people don't marry for love. Women just have to be a bit more discreet then us men. I have found it easier to have affairs with married women rather than single ones because I knew that if one of them became pregnant, she would just pass off the pregnancy as her husband's child. However, unmarried women becoming pregnant would be seen as a disgrace.

Even my wife Alix doesn't seem to mind Alice. I think she finds her very discreet and respectful and doesn't go around flaunting the fact that she is having an affair with me. I am fully aware that politicians like to become friends with Alice to try to get her to influence me. Of course, Alix can't have affairs. It wouldn't be acceptable for a Queen to do that.

Extra-marital affairs can be complicated though. A few years back, in 1891, I fell out with a friend, Lord Charles Beresford, because he accused me of interfering in his relationship with

Daisy Greville, Countess of Warwick, who went on to become one of my long-term mistresses. He tried to blackmail me by threatening to release details about my private life to the press. Daisy got into problems of her own and I knew she had a few affairs too. While she was seeing Charles, she wrote a letter to him which was unfortunately intercepted by his wife. This caused quite a scandal at the time. I tried to get Lady Beresford to give up the letter but she gave Lady Warwick a choice: stay away from London for the season and the letter would be returned to her. Even the Prime Minister, Lord Salisbury, had to intervene at one point. Anyway, Charles and I had quite an argument over it and he even pushed me up against the sofa. I forgave him in the end but we didn't stay friends after that. Lady Warwick also had affairs with other people. She got pregnant when she was having an affair with someone else and obviously I couldn't see her at that point.

That wasn't the first time my affairs landed me in trouble. I was once called as a witness in the divorce case of another of my mistresses, Lady Mordant. When her husband, Sir Charles, found out about our affair, he got quite upset and decided to divorce her in 1869. She had given birth to a child who had inherited a sexually transmitted disease. Her own family branded her insane because they couldn't live with the scandal. She ended up being placed in an asylum for 36 years – the rest of her life. My mother had to step in to ensure the scandal was played to a minimum because this was embarrassing to the Royal Family and the monarchy. She asked the press to keep it quiet. Luckily I was only asked a few questions when I appeared in court.

I'm afraid I got myself in other kinds of trouble too, like in 1891 when I was caught being involved in an illegal card game. Once again, I had to appear in court as a witness.

So perhaps it is not surprising that my mother didn't approve of my affairs, or even my friendships. But then she didn't even approve of Alix's friends, who were in every way beyond reproach.

I have been an active King for nine years now and I take a keen interest in state affairs. There was a bit of a scare just after I became King because I got appendicitis and had to have an operation to remove my appendix, which meant that my coronation was postponed. Mama was a very popular Queen and was a hard act to follow. But over time I myself became more popular. I would like to think that I will be remembered as a good King who reinvigorated the monarchy. My son, George, will most likely succeed me.

Postscript: When Edward VII was on his death bed, his wife, Alexandra, allowed Alice Keppel to go and see him. Despite the large age gap of almost 30 years, Edward and Alice had true feelings for one another. Edward VII died on 6 May 1910 aged 68 and was succeeded by his son, George V. Some historians believe that Edward had ADHD (attention deficit hyperactivity disorder), which may have accounted for his short attention span as a child.

Prince Albert Victor
Duke of Clarence and Avondale

Born 8 January 1864 – died 14 January 1892

I am the eldest son of the Prince and Princess of Wales (later Edward VII and Queen Alexandra). I am known as Eddy to my family and friends. I have a younger brother and three younger sisters. As a child, I got on well with my parents and was very close to my brother, George, who is only 17 months younger than me. We visited Denmark every summer to see my cousins and maternal grandparents, who were King Christian IX and Queen Louise of Denmark. We were educated at home, Marlborough House in London. I am second in line to the throne so I have always felt there were greater expectations on me than on George. When I was 13, we were both sent to join the Royal Navy, where we studied at the Royal Naval Academy on HMS Britannia, accompanied by our dreadfully dull tutor. We then went on a three-year world tour with the Navy, visiting much of the British Empire, including the Americas, South Africa, Australia, the Far East and the Middle East. Whilst we were in Japan we even got tattoos.

We returned to Britain when I was 18. I was sent to Trinity College, University of Cambridge, because it was thought that I should receive a university education as I will eventually become King. I even spent a bit of time at Heidelberg University studying German, as the ability to speak several languages is seen as very important for a future monarch. I learnt Danish from my mother and also studied French. I enjoyed

my time at Cambridge on a social level but I admit I am not really much of an academic. Luckily I did not have to take exams and I was awarded an honorary degree. I enjoy sports like hunting and shooting.

After university, I spent my time undertaking royal duties and I visited Ireland and Gibraltar. The Queen was restricted by the government from travelling abroad because they were concerned for her safety because she has been subjected to a number of assassination attempts. Fortunately, no one has attempted to assassinate me.

My family are keen for me to marry as it is my duty to produce heirs to the throne and they have tried to pair me up with a number of women over the last few years. First of all, my family wanted me to marry my cousin, Alix. I admit I was fond of her but she was in love with the Tsarevich (the future Tsar Nicholas II). Later, in 1890, I was in a serious relationship with Princess Hélène d'Orleans. She was from France but living in exile in England. We wanted to marry and we asked my grandmother, Queen Victoria, for permission to marry. At first, she was absolutely opposed to it because Hélène was Catholic but after Hélène said that she would convert to the Church of England, we won Grandmamma over. Unfortunately, there was still a lot of opposition, particularly from her family, so we had to part. We were both devastated, as we were very much in love. My family then suggested that I marry another cousin, Princess Margaret of Prussia, but I am not interested in her.

Recently there have been rumours in the foreign press about me being involved with a chorus girl called Lydia. She committed suicide by drinking carbolic acid but I have not had a relationship with her. The latest proposal from my family is that I marry Princess Mary of Teck. I have agreed to marry her but I don't love her as I am still in love with Hélène. We are due to marry on 27 February 1892.

Postscript: Albert Victor fell ill with influenza, which developed into pneumonia. He died at Sandringham on 14 January 1892, surrounded by his parents, his siblings, Mary of Teck and her parents. He was only 28. His father, the Prince of Wales, wrote to Queen Victoria: "Gladly I would have given my life for his." His mother, Alexandra of Denmark, never fully recovered from his death and kept the room where he died preserved as a shrine. He was buried at the Albert Memorial Chapel, close to St George's Chapel in Windsor.

King George V

Born 3 June 1865 – died 20 January 1936

Growing up, and as a young man, I was not expecting to become King. I am the second son of Edward VII and Alexandra of Denmark, so my older brother Eddy (Albert Victor) was heir to the throne. But at 27, he was suddenly taken ill with pneumonia and died and I became the second in line to the throne after my father, who was Prince of Wales at the time. I was devastated by my brother's death, as I was very close to him, but I was also shocked about the prospect of becoming King one day, as it was not something I particularly wanted or had expected.

I was born at Marlborough House in London and I was only 17 months younger than Eddy. We were educated together but neither of us were very intellectually inclined. At 12, my brother and I joined the Royal Navy, which I loved. We were sent to the cadet training ship, HMS Britannia, in Devon. We went on a three-year world tour with the Navy. In Japan we both got tattoos – mine was a blue and red dragon on my arm. Whilst

there, we met the Emperor and Empress of Japan and I found the country fascinating, as it was so different from England.

On returning to England, my grandmother, Queen Victoria, complained that neither of us could speak French or German, so we had to spend six months in Switzerland in an unsuccessful attempt to learn another language. I barely speak Danish, which is my mother's language. After that, my brother was sent to university but I stayed on in the Navy until my brother died, when I became second in line to the throne. During my time in the Navy, I was particularly close to Uncle Alfred, who was also in the Navy, and I served under his command in Malta. I also became close to his family and in particular my cousin Missy (Princess Marie). Our fathers and our grandmother, Queen Victoria, all wanted us to marry but our mothers were not pleased with the prospect. My mother thought the family was too pro-German. Missy was very close to her mother, who I think influenced her against me as she refused my proposal.

After Eddy died, it was decided that I would marry my late brother's fiancée, Princess Mary of Teck, who I call May. We became close after Eddy died and I proposed to her a year later. We married on 6 July 1893 at the Chapel Royal, St James' Palace. We lived much of the time in York Cottage, Sandringham, as we preferred to live in the country. We had six children: five boys and a girl. Our youngest son, John, had fairly serious epilepsy and was unable to perform any royal duties or go out in public. From the time of my marriage until I became Prince of Wales, I was known as the Duke of York, and during that period I was able to spend a lot of my time doing my two favourite hobbies, which were hunting and stamp-collecting.

My grandmother died in 1901, my father ascended the throne and I became Prince of Wales. This meant that I had more royal duties and had a larger presence in public life. May and I toured the British Empire – we went to many countries including Gibraltar, Ceylon (Sri Lanka), Singapore, Australia, South Africa and Canada. Australia became a self-governing colony, so I opened the first session of the new Australian parliament. The whole trip took about a year and we had to leave the children behind in England, so it felt like a really long time. When I returned, my father included me in state affairs because he was keen to prepare me for my future role as King. He was determined that I should not be treated as his mother had treated him because she had excluded him from state affairs. When I became King, I allowed my wife access to state papers because I valued her counsel and she helped to write my speeches.

In the winter of 1905/06, May and I toured British India, which I enjoyed, but I was most disgusted by the racial discrimination of the native population. The British people seemed rather arrogant, which I found quite unsettling. We then went to Spain for my cousin Victoria Eugenie's wedding to King Alfonso XIII. As they were returning back to the Palace for the wedding reception, there was a terrorist attack. Someone threw a bomb at them but miraculously they were unhurt, even though their guards and many people in the crowd died.

On 6 May 1910, my father died and I became King, at the age of 45. My father was my best friend and I never had a cross word with him in my life. I felt apprehensive about being King, as I was aware of the huge responsibility. May and I were both crowned in Westminster Abbey on 22 June 1911. We visited Ireland, where we received a warm welcome. Later that year, we travelled to India again, which was the first time a British monarch had gone there. We had a Delhi Durbar, where we were proclaimed as Emperor and Empress of India. I wore the Imperial Crown of India, which had been especially made for the occasion. We enjoyed India and the hunting was wonderful.

During my reign, the Great War broke out, which was a terrible catastrophe. As you would expect, there was widespread anti-German sentiment in the country at the time. H G Wells accused my court of being alien and uninspiring. I replied that "I may be uninspiring, but I will be dammed if I'm alien". We never considered ourselves German but it was decided that our family name should be changed from the German-sounding name of Saxe-Coburg to Windsor. I also recommended that my cousins, the Battenbergs (Aunt Beatrice's children), change their name to Mountbatten. This also gave me the opportunity to streamline the Royal Family to limit the number of princes and princesses.

I stripped Aunt Beatrice's children of their royal status. I allowed Aunt Helena's children to keep their royal titles but asked them to give up their German territorial designations, as I felt that Uncle Christian (Aunt Helena's husband), who was the last surviving son-in-law of Queen Victoria, was deserving of some respect. Also, the Duke of Saxe-Coburg and Gotha was stripped of his British nationality but his sister, Alice, remained British but gave up her German nationality. This meant that I reserved the title of Prince and Princess to the children of the Sovereign and the children of the sons of the Sovereign. So my daughter's children are not considered royal and are not known as Princes, although, of course, they are still considered part of the Royal Family.

Following the Russian Revolution in 1917, my cousin, Tsar Nicholas II of Russia, wanted to seek asylum in England with his family. I initially wanted him to come but my private secretary convinced me that this was a terrible idea and that it could result in the end of the monarchy here. It was my sacred duty to ensure the survival of the monarchy in Britain, so that the nation would not descend into republican anarchy. However, I felt devastated when I heard that Nicholas and his family were murdered in Russia. Later, I sent a warship to rescue Aunt Minnie (Nicholas' mother, former Empress Maria Feodorovna) and some other members of the extended Russian Imperial Family to bring them to England.

My German cousins were forced to abdicate at the end of the Great War and obviously they could not come and live here either, although some of them did visit from time to time when things had settled down. Sadly, just two months after the war ended, my youngest son, John, died from an epileptic fit when he was only 13.

Following the war, there was a lot of political change in this country. Socialism was on the rise and in 1922 Ireland became independent from the United Kingdom. During the Great Depression of 1929, I encouraged the formation of a National Government to help solve the economic crisis. One of the reasons that I think the monarchy in Russia and Germany failed was because they were too aloof from the people. I felt that I should modernise the monarchy by doing walkabouts and meeting the people. In 1932, I made my first Christmas speech on the radio and it was so well received that it has now become an annual event.

I believe I was a good father, although I'm not sure all my children would agree. I find my eldest, David (who later became Edward VIII), wilful and insolent. He is very hedonistic and seems to have no reverence for the Christian faith. I worry about what sort of King he will be. I have tried to prepare him to be King but I think that within a year the boy will ruin himself. He is 30 and is still not married, which I am disappointed about. I want him to marry for love but I also want him to marry someone of good moral standing. I strongly disapprove of all the affairs he has with married women and I am certainly not happy that he is in a relationship with Wallis Simpson, an American woman who has been divorced twice. I actually think that my second son Bertie (later George VI) would make a better King than David. I am also concerned about the rise of Nazism in Germany and think if things go on like this there will be another war within 10 years.

Postscript: George V's health declined after the First World War. He suffered from bronchitis and chronic breathing problems made worse by smoking. In December 1935, his favourite sister, Victoria, died and he plunged into a deep depression. In January 1936, George V took to his bed at Sandringham, complaining of a cold. His health deteriorated and he died on 20 January 1936, aged 70. He was succeeded by his son David (Edward VIII), who abdicated by the end of that year. Bertie (George VI) then ascended the throne.

Princess Louise
Princess Royal, Duchess of Fife

Born 20 February 1867 – died 4 January 1931

My parents were Edward VII and Alexandra of Denmark. I had two older siblings and two younger ones. We were all very close in age and I was especially close to my sisters growing up. We lived at Marlborough House in London and also stayed at our Sandringham residence.

In 1889, when I was 22, I married Alexander Duff, the Earl of Fife. He was 18 years older than me. Despite the large age gap, we married for love. Two days after our wedding, my grandmother, Queen Victoria, elevated him to the rank of Duke. We lived at his main residence in Fife, Scotland, and also in London because as a Duke, he sat in the House of Lords. He had a political and diplomatic career, while I led a quiet, retiring life and preferred to live in the countryside in Scotland.

My brothers both became ill in 1892. Eddy (Albert Victor) contracted double pneumonia following an influenza epidemic, from which he sadly died, and George contracted typhoid but he fortunately survived and became heir to the throne. At the

time, people began to talk about the possibility of them both dying. Obviously that would have been devastating for all of us as a family but for me personally that prospect would have put me in line to the throne after my father, which was something that I would have dreaded. I am not cut out for that life as I am very shy and don't like taking part in public life. Also, as I was married to a commoner by then, I don't think many people from high society would have wanted me to become Queen. By 1894, George had married and had a son, so obviously I went down in the line of succession, which suited me fine.

My first child was stillborn. The doctors don't know why he died but we named him Alistair. After that terrible experience, I fortunately had two healthy daughters, Alexandra and Maud. Alexandra was named after my mother and Maud after my sister. My daughters were not royal and they were known as Lady Alexandra and Lady Maud. However, after my father became King he gave me the title of Princess Royal, as I was the eldest daughter of the monarch, and so our daughters became Princesses. They were 14 and 12 at the time.

In 1911, as Alexander and I were en route to Egypt, we were shipwrecked off the coast of Morocco. After spending hours in a lifeboat we were finally rescued and made it to land, but then we had to walk for miles in pouring rain before reaching shelter. Obviously, this was quite a traumatic experience. Alexander developed pleurisy, probably as a result of this ordeal, and shortly after we got to Egypt he very sadly died. This was particularly ironic as the reason we were going there in the first place was because we thought the warmer climate would be good for his health. This was probably one of the worst experiences of my life, along with my stillbirth. Alexander was 62 when he died. We were able to bring his body home and he was buried at Windsor. Alexandra succeeded her father as Duchess of Fife in her own right.

Alexandra married Prince Arthur, Uncle Arthur's son, and they had a son called Alistair, named after my son who had died at birth. Maud also married and became Countess of Southesk and had a son called James.

Postscript: In the autumn of 1929, Louise was taken ill with gastric haemorrhage and she died on 4 January 1931, aged 63. She was buried beside her husband at Windsor.

Princess Victoria

Born 6 July 1868 – died 3 December 1935

My family and friends call me Toria and I am the daughter of King Edward VII and Alexandra of Denmark. I had four siblings: two brothers and two sisters. We lived at Marlborough House in London and also in Sandringham. My childhood was unremarkable and I was educated at home.

Although I had some suitors I never married. One of the most notable was King Carlos of Portugal but I turned him down. In his case, religion would have been a problem because he was Catholic. To be honest, I had no desire to get married. I preferred to stay at home and live with my parents and be a companion to them, particularly to my mother. My mother was a bit lonely as social functions were an ordeal for her because she had a hearing impairment. Although my parents got on with each other, she had to endure my father's many affairs. She never openly talked about how she felt about his affairs. Maybe she thought it was just something she had to put up with, as it was not uncommon for men in his position to have them. I was 24 when my eldest brother Eddy died (Albert Victor). It was very upsetting, particularly for my mother, who I don't think ever really got over his death.

When I was younger, I did go travelling to visit family in England and Germany. I also got involved with some of the charities of which my mother was patron as Queen. I very much enjoyed being an aunt to my siblings' children, particularly George and Louise's children. I have always stayed very close to George and my sisters.

After my father died in 1910, my brother George became King. I lived through the Great War, which has changed the world so much. Before the war, many European countries had monarchies, but after the war many monarchs were forced to abdicate.

My mother died in 1925, when I was 57. I was very sad and found her death very difficult, as I had lived with her all my life. I then set up my own home in Buckinghamshire and my main interest now is horticulture. I enjoy taking part in village life but I am still fairly near London, which is useful when I want to go there. My sister Maud, who is now Queen of Norway, comes to visit England every summer.

I am 67 now. In recent years I have been suffering from health problems like neuralgia, migraines, indigestion and also depression.

Postscript: Victoria died in 1935 at her home in Buckinghamshire and she was buried in Windsor. Her death greatly affected George V, as she was his favourite sister, and he died one month later.

Queen Maud

of Norway

Born 26 November 1869 – died 20 November 1938

I am the youngest child of Edward VII and Alexandra of Denmark and was born at Marlborough House, London. My sisters and I were probably closer to our mother than other children of our class, as she spent quite a bit of time with us. I think my mother probably didn't want us to get married. I didn't marry until my late twenties. which was quite old for that time period. My sister Toria (Victoria) didn't marry at all. Initially, I wanted to marry Prince Francis, Queen Mary's brother, but he was not interested.

In 1896, I married my maternal first cousin, Prince Carl of Denmark. He was the second son of Uncle Frederick, who was the Crown Prince of Denmark, and I went to live in Denmark. Our mutual grandfather was King Christian IX of Denmark. Carl's father, Frederick, succeeded the throne in 1906 and his brother became King in 1912.

At the time we married, I thought that as minor royals of the Danish Royal Family we would live a quiet life, but life is

full of surprises and things rarely turn out the way we expect. In 1905, Norway achieved independence from neighbouring Sweden, and Carl was asked to become the King of Norway. He is a very liberal and democratically-minded man, so he insisted that they hold a referendum to find out the will of the people. The referendum result confirmed an overwhelming majority of the Norwegian people wished him to become King, so he did, and I became Queen. It was a little ironic that Norway wanted Carl to be their King, as he was a grandson of the Swedish King and his mother was Swedish. However, I think that Carl having an English wife may have influenced their decision, as Great Britain is known for its democracy, something which they wanted for Norway. Carl changed his name and became Haakon VII of Norway.

So we moved to Norway and I learnt Norwegian fairly easily, as I already could speak Danish, which I had learnt from my mother, and the two languages are similar. The cold, dark winters are an aspect of living in Norway that took some getting used to but the summers are warmer and have long days of light. I learnt all the winter sports, including skiing, which is practically compulsory in Norway.

We have been very happily married and we have one son, Olav, who was born in 1903 in England while I was visiting for the summer. When he was born, we named him Alexander, but he was given the name Olav when Carl ascended the Norwegian throne. He has grown up, married Princess Martha of Sweden and they have three children: Ragnhild, Astrid and Harald. My husband is still on the throne and his elder brother is on the Danish throne, so the two countries have close relations.

Being the first King and Queen of Norway for several centuries meant that there was really no precedent for us but we felt it important to integrate into the Norwegian aristocracy and into Norwegian culture. For example, we were photographed in Norwegian folk costumes and took up winter sports. I don't take part very much in public life because I think that my husband, the King, should be at the forefront. Obviously, I accompany him when needed but I dislike the representational duties of Queen and I only do them because I have to. I like to spend my time supporting charitable causes involving children and animals. I support a home for unwed mothers, which is not a popular thing to do in our society. In my spare time I enjoy horse-riding.

We still have strong family ties with the Danish and the British Royal Families. I also have cousins all over Europe, including Germany. However, I still regard England as my true home and until recently I visited every summer to see my brother George and my sisters. Sadly George and Toria both died three years ago and I have just witnessed the scandal of my nephew David (Edward VIII) abdicating the throne and his brother Bertie (George VI) taking his place.

Postscript: In October 1938, Maud went to England and stayed at Sandringham. She fell ill and needed an operation. Haakon immediately travelled there to be with her but she died unexpectedly of heart failure in November, aged 68. Her body was returned to Norway and she is buried at the Royal Mausoleum in Oslo.

During World War Two, Norway was invaded by the Nazis so Haakon and the government fled Oslo and went to the very north of Norway. They did not surrender to the Nazis and Sweden refused to give them refuge but they were able to escape to England, where a government in exile was set up. Haakon broadcast radio messages to the Norwegian people, urging them not to give them up. A puppet government was set up in Oslo and the Nazis attempted to abolish the monarchy but faced strong resistance from the Norwegian people. After the war, the Norwegian Royal Family returned and they received widespread public support.

Haakon VII died in 1957, aged 85. He was succeeded by their son Olav, whose wife Martha had already passed away. Haakon and Maud's grandson, Harald, succeeded him in 1991.

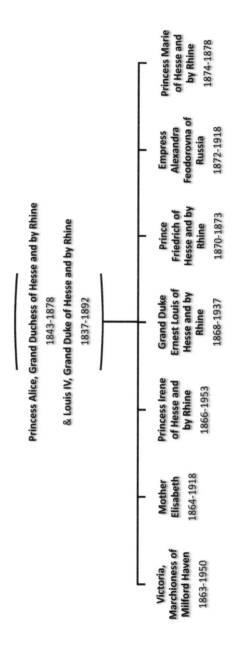

Family Tree of Princess Alice

Third Child of Queen Victoria

Princess Alice, Grand Duchess of Hesse and by Rhine
1843-1878

& Louis IV, Grand Duke of Hesse and by Rhine
1837-1892

Victoria, Marchioness of Milford Haven
1863-1950

Mother Elisabeth
1864-1918

Princess Irene of Hesse and by Rhine
1866-1953

Grand Duke Ernest Louis of Hesse and by Rhine
1868-1937

Prince Friedrich of Hesse and by Rhine
1870-1873

Empress Alexandra Feodorovna of Russia
1872-1918

Princess Marie of Hesse and by Rhine
1874-1878

Princess Alice

Grand Duchess of Hesse and by Rhine

Born 25 April 1843 – died 14 December 1878

I am the third child of Queen Victoria and Prince Albert. I had a sheltered upbringing and few friends, apart from my siblings. I was closest to my sister Victoria, my elder brother Bertie, and Affie, who was a year younger than me. I was very sad when my sister Victoria was married and went to live in Prussia, as I missed her terribly. From a young age, I was always fascinated by the lives of ordinary people and I wanted to understand them more. At Balmoral, I would visit the tenants who lived on the estate to get to know them, so that I could try to understand what it was like to live a less privileged life. On one occasion, at Windsor, I even managed to escape from my governess so I could sit with the ordinary people in church. As I grew older, my interest in ordinary people's lives developed into a desire to try to improve their living standards.

My family were looking for a good marriage for me. I was initially introduced to the Prince of Orange and then Prince Albert of Prussia, a cousin of Fritz, my sister's husband. I met the Prince of Orange at Windsor Castle but I didn't really like him, so no marriage materialised and I don't think he was very interested in me either. I didn't care much for Prince Albert of Prussia and besides, Fritz thought he wouldn't do for me. Finally, I was introduced to Prince Louis of Hesse. My sister Vicky (Victoria) enjoyed being a matchmaker and after unsuccessfully trying to pair Louis'

sister, Anna, with our brother, Bertie, she suggested Louis as a match for me. We had a courtship and he seemed pleasant and I believed in the beginning that I loved him. Of course, the number of potential suitors was limited because I was expected to marry royalty from one country or another. He was a German Prince and in line to inherit the Ducal throne of Hesse and by Rhine. My parents were pro-German and they were looking to strengthen the political relationship between the two countries.

I was 18 when we got married and he was six years older than me. Our wedding was very small and private. It was held at Osborne House on the Isle of Wight. The Court was still in mourning for my father, who had died seven months earlier so everyone was wearing black. My mother allowed me to wear a white wedding dress for the actual ceremony but she sat sobbing through the whole thing so, to be honest, it wasn't that pleasant. I was quite relieved to be leaving the British Court, even though I did feel a bit sorry for Mama.

We had seven children: two boys and five girls. Ernest, my eldest, will inherit the throne after his father. I lost Frittie (Frederick) when he was only two years old. He had haemophilia, a disease that seems to run in my family. He was playing with his brother Ernest when he fell out of a window. The doctors said he would have survived if he didn't have the disease. He bled to death and never regained consciousness. It was very traumatic and I am still terribly sad about that. I knew he had the disease but I don't know much about it. My brother, Leopold, has it too – he was the first person in the United Kingdom to be diagnosed with it. We are not sure where it came from. Fortunately, my other children all seem to be of good health.

I have some religious views which were sometimes a problem for the rest of German high society. I became friendly with a theologian called David Frederick Strauss and he believes that the Bible cannot be interpreted literally. I agree with a lot of what he says. Some people aren't too happy with this and about me introducing him to my sister Vicky and her husband Fritz. Her mother-in-law has branded me a complete atheist, which I'm not. I am a Christian but I just don't have traditional views. I don't believe all the Bible stories, like Jonah being swallowed by a whale.

Louis ascended the Grand Ducal throne in 1877 after we had been married for 15 years. The social functions of the Court are not really something I enjoy. I fulfil my duties but I don't particularly enjoy them. Since my husband became Grand Duke, I am obviously expected to accompany him and socialise with the other ladies of the Court. Louis is a bit more involved in politics and government than my mother, Queen Victoria, who is a constitutional monarch. I leave all that to him. My sister Vicky is the political one in the family. I am more interested in social and charitable causes. Nursing, for example, is my passion in life. I would have loved to have been a nurse had I not been born into the Royal Family but I have opened a hospital in

Darmstadt providing free medical care, which is unusual here. It is funded by donations and I spend a lot of time fundraising and would like to open more hospitals. I also correspond with Florence Nightingale, a pioneering nurse. I make sure the hospital is up-to-date with all the latest medical equipment. I did nurse briefly during the Austrian-Prussian War of 1866, tending to the soldiers, but that was only for a few weeks.

I'm still close to my older siblings, although it was a little difficult in 1866 when my husband and Vicky's husband fought on opposite sides. Although Prussia won the war and it annexed a number of principalities, it did not annex most of our Grand Duchy. This was good because otherwise it may have caused tension between Vicky and me. I have a difficult relationship with my mother. She has never been the same since Papa died. After he died and before I was married I served as her unofficial press secretary, so I did grow close to her for a time. She lived in seclusion so I acted as her intermediary with the outside world. I helped her with government papers and that sort of thing. But after I was married we became more distant. Now I find her very argumentative. She disapproves of my interest in biology, saying it is inappropriate for a princess, she disapproved of me breastfeeding my children, she got annoyed when I criticised her for trying to pair up my sister Helena with her husband. We also disagreed when my brother Affie got married to the Russian Grand Duchess Maria. I suggested that we all met up in Germany but she got all difficult about that and so she never met the Russian family in the end. I don't see that much of her now and we communicate mainly by letter.

Victoria, my eldest daughter, contracted diphtheria in November 1878 but then it quickly spread to the other members of the family. Ella (Elizabeth) was sent to stay with relatives so she was the only member who escaped the illness. I helped nurse everyone. My baby Marie caught it and died. She was only four years old but I still thought of her as my baby. I can't describe the pain at losing another child. I decided not to tell my other children that she had died because I didn't want to upset them, but I finally told Ernest and, at first, he didn't even believe me.

Postscript: A short time later Alice also contracted diphtheria and died on 14 December 1878, the anniversary of her father's death. She was only 35. This was particularly hard for Queen Victoria, who had never really got over Prince Albert's death, and the family always met up on the anniversary of his death. Alice was the first of Queen Victoria's children to die, Victoria outliving her by over 20 years. Queen Victoria wrote "This terrible day come round again. My precious child, who stood by me and upheld me 17 years ago, on the same day taken, and by such an awful and fearful disease. She had darling Papa's nature and much of his self-sacrificing character and fearless devotion to duty."

Victoria
Marchioness of Milford Haven

Born 5 April 1863 – died 24 September 1950

My parents were Louis IV, Grand Duke of Hesse and by Rhine, and Princess Alice. At the time of my birth I was known as Princess Victoria of Hesse and by Rhine. Now I am an 87-year-old Dowager Marchioness and I live in Kensington Palace.

I was born in Windsor Castle, as I think my mother wanted to have her first child near her own mother, Queen Victoria, but I grew up in Darmstadt, Germany. I had six younger siblings, although two died young. From a royal perspective, we had a very simple life as we were the Royal Family of a tiny principality. My father became the Grand Duke in 1877. I shared a room with my sister Ella and we were educated at home. When I was three, I was sent to England for the duration of the Seven Weeks' War between Prussia and Austria. Later, during the Franco-Prussian War of 1870-71, I helped my mother in the soup kitchens which were set up in the palace grounds to feed the soldiers. I remember the winter was very harsh that year and I burnt my

*Princess Victoria with her husband,
Prince Louis of Battenberg*

arm from the hot soup. When I was only 10, my younger brother, Frittie, died.

At the age of 15, I along with the rest of the family got diphtheria. Ella was the only one who escaped it as she was sent away to relatives. My youngest sister, Marie, who was only four, and my mother, Alice, both died from the illness. That was obviously very traumatic for all of us and it meant that my childhood was effectively over. It fell to me, as the oldest sibling, to take over the responsibility of mothering my brother and sisters.

At family gatherings, I would see Prince Louis of Battenberg, who was my first cousin once removed. Over time we fell in love and we married in Darmstadt on 30 April 1884. My father did not approve of the match because Louis was not very wealthy and also because we intended to live abroad, but I was determined to marry him. My siblings and I were all horrified on my wedding day to find out that my father had secretly married his mistress, a divorcee. I was unhappy about his double standards and it became quite a scandal. However, he was eventually forced to seek an annulment of his marriage because not only was she divorced but she was of unequal rank to him, as she was a Russian commoner. My siblings and I found the marriage insensitive and a betrayal of our mother's memory.

Louis and I settled in England, although we did move around a bit as he was in the British Navy. However, because of his German origins, he was deprived of his office at the start of the First World War, so he did not take part in it. Three years into our marriage, I had typhoid but fortunately I recovered. We had four children: Alice, Louise, George and Louis. We lived a fairly quiet life as minor royals. Alice was sadly born deaf but she has learnt to lip-read, so she gets along quite well. My sons, George and Louis, both joined the Navy and they were able to take part in the war and fortunately they both survived. We were very lucky, as many families lost someone during that war. When the war broke out, my daughter Louise and I were in Russia so we had to return quickly to England.

I am interested in science and I enjoy taking part in archaeological digs, which I did in Germany and Malta. I also love reading a wide range of books. I taught my own children when they were young. I have flown in a zeppelin airship and in a plane before the First World War, in the very early days of flying.

In 1917 George V decided that his German relatives living in Britain which included me, should give up our German royal titles. We changed our family name from Battenberg to Mountbatten, which is really the English version of the name. In compensation for the loss of our titles, my husband was ennobled as the Marquess of Milford Haven and I became the Marchioness. He was offered a Dukedom but he declined due to the extravagant lifestyle that Dukes are expected to keep.

Up until 1914 I would visit my German and Russian relatives but this became impossible during the war. After the war, I received the news that my two sisters, Alix and Ella, who had married into the Russian Royal Family, had been murdered, which was horrifying and desperately sad. After the war my brother Ernest Louis lost his Ducal throne, along with all the other German royals who were forced to abdicate. Fortunately,

I was again able to visit my surviving siblings, Ernest Louis and Irene, in Germany, which had not been possible during the war.

Since the end of the First World War, I feel my life has been fraught with many tragedies and difficulties. My husband died suddenly of heart failure in 1921. I was at the pharmacist getting his medicine but when I returned he had died. After that, I moved into Kensington Palace, where I still live.

My daughter Louise married the Crown Prince of Sweden, Gustav Adolph, in 1923 at St James Palace. She was 34, which was considered quite old then to get married, but I was delighted. However, sadly she gave birth to a stillborn daughter two years later and has not been able to have more children.

In 1930 my daughter Alice was institutionalised as she was diagnosed with schizophrenia, although she is better now and has been released. During that time, I looked after my grandson, Philip, who has now married Princess Elizabeth (the present Queen).

In 1937 my brother Ernest Louis died and a month later his son, who was married to my grand-daughter Cecily, two of their children and their unborn child all died in a plane crash. That was a really difficult time as I lost my grand-daughter and two great grandchildren. In the same year my son George also died from bone cancer.

During the Second World War my son Louis and my grandson Philip served in the Royal Navy but I was more worried about my daughter Alice because she was living in Nazi-occupied Greece, as she had married into the Greek Royal Family. During that time she risked her own life to protect some Jewish families by hiding them in her own home. I didn't know that at the time as we were not able to communicate with each other during the war but I am very proud of what she did.

After the war my son Louis became the Viceroy of India and during that time India became independent.

I am now 87 and have bronchitis. I feel I have seen a lot

in my life, including many tragedies. I have lived through two world wars, many monarchs and even through the abdication crisis of Edward VIII in 1936.

Postscript: Victoria fell ill with bronchitis and died at home on 24 September 1950. She was buried alongside her husband in St Mildred's Church on the Isle of Wight.

Mother Elisabeth

Abbess of St Martha and Mary Convent, Moscow

Born 1 November 1864 – died 18 July 1918

I was born Princess Elisabeth of Hesse and by Rhine, daughter of Grand Duke Louis IV and Princess Alice. I was named after my paternal grandmother Princess Elisabeth of Prussia as well as Saint Elisabeth of Hungary, who had inspired my mother.

I had a modest childhood by royal standards and I was always very conscious of my half English, half German identity. I can speak English as well as I can speak German. We were a tight-knit family but I was particularly close to my mother and my older sister Victoria, with whom I shared a room. In 1878 all my family fell ill with diphtheria, except for me, as I had been sent away to my paternal grandmother's home. My mother and baby sister died from the illness, which was a terrible time for all of us, especially as I was only 14 at the time.

As a young woman, I had many admirers and suitors, including my cousin, Wilhelm of Prussia, who later became the German Emperor. He often came to visit and he proposed to

me but I said no. The future Grand
Duke of Baden also proposed but
I refused him too. I wanted to
marry for love and eventually I fell
in love with Sergei Alexandrovich,
Grand Duke of Russia, my first
cousin once removed. We had
known each other since we were
children but when we met again
as adults, we found we had a lot
in common and we fell in love.
My grandmother, Queen Victoria,

was against our marriage, as she did not care for Russia, and
she tried to talk me out of marrying Sergei. At one point she
briefly succeeded when I broke off our engagement. However,
Sergei soon won me over again and our engagement was back
on. We married in 1884 in the chapel of the Winter Palace in St
Petersburg and I became Grand Duchess Elizabeth Feodorovna
of Russia. He was Tsar Alexander III's younger brother and uncle
to Tsar Nicholas II. Although I was not required to convert to
Russian Orthodoxy, as I had only married the Tsar's younger
brother, I did decide to convert a few years later in 1891.

My life in Russia was very different from what I had been
used to as a child. The Russian Imperial Court was very grand
and the palaces were very opulent and luxurious. The Court
etiquette was much more formal and they spoke French. I
spoke some French and I also learnt Russian. My husband was
appointed the Governor General of Moscow, so we went to live
there.

We were happily married but sadly were unable to have
children of our own. However, we looked after my brother-in-
law's children, Maria and Dimitri, because their mother had
died and their father abandoned them to marry his mistress.
He was sent into exile for marrying someone who was not royal

and he was not allowed to take his children with him. Dimitri and Maria were 11 and 12 years old when they came to live with us. As much as I like children, it was quite difficult to have them. Maria, especially, had some emotional issues, having been abandoned by her father, and they possibly blamed us for their separation from their father.

I encouraged my husband's nephew, Nicholas, to pursue my sister Alix. She was reluctant to convert to Russian Orthodoxy, which was a requirement, as Nicholas would later become Tsar, but I persuaded her. They were married in 1894 – 10 years after us.

In 1905 Sergei was assassinated. He had just resigned as Governor General of Moscow and he was about to clear out his office in the Kremlin when a revolutionary threw a bomb into his carriage, which killed him. I remember rushing out into the street where I was so distressed when I saw what had happened to my beloved husband that I tried to gather up Sergei's remains. I went to visit his murderer in prison so that I could ask why he had killed my husband and he replied that "he (Sergei) was a weapon of tyranny and he was taking revenge for the people". I forgave him and gave him a Bible in the hope that he would repent. I interceded with the Tsar for his life but he was executed despite my plea. Sergei's death was devastating for me and it changed my life, but I still had the two children to look after. Maria, in particular, became a great comfort to me in the early days after Sergei's death. I became much closer to God and found solace in Him. I became a vegetarian for religious reasons and I felt God calling me to become a nun.

A few years later I arranged a marriage for Maria with Prince Wilhelm of Sweden. In hindsight that turned out to be a terrible choice and their marriage ended in divorce. Dimitri also grew up and didn't need me anymore, so I was free to become a nun. I sold off all my jewels and other possessions and I gave a third of the income to the Russian Crown, another third to relatives and the rest was used to open the Convent of St Martha and Mary. In the grounds we opened a hospital, a pharmacy and an orphanage. I became the Abbess and other Sisters joined me. We went out into the slums of Moscow to look after the poor and the sick. Although I miss Sergei, I have found happiness and have no regrets.

I have kept in touch with the family mainly by letter, although some of them do visit me, especially Maria, my foster daughter, now she is back in Russia following her divorce. She has found love again with Prince Sergei Putyatin. He is lower than her in rank but I am happy for her.

At present, Russia is at war with my native Germany and there is a lot of unrest in Russia and dissatisfaction with the Great War, partly because of all the lost lives. Tsar Nicholas II went to lead from the front and left my sister as Regent. Some members of the family persuaded me to try to convince my sister that Rasputin was a terrible influence on the family. I don't like to intervene in politics because I don't know much about that, but in this instance I believed it was for the good of Russia. I went to see my sister Alix and I tried to warn her that everyone believed Rasputin wielded too much influence in Russia but she wouldn't hear of it. She seemed to be under his spell and it was most distressing. As Regent, whenever Alix had to make a decision, she asked Rasputin what to do, so the whole country was under the direction of this false 'holy' man.

A short while later Rasputin was murdered by a group of conspirators, one of whom was my foster son Dimitri. Subsequently, Tsar Nicholas sent them into exile. The Russian people were celebrating in the streets that Rasputin was gone. Tsar Nicholas was forced to abdicate following the Revolution in 1917 and he and the family were sent to Siberia under house arrest. I haven't seen them since and am terribly worried what is going to happen to them.

Postscript: In 1918 Elisabeth, along with several other members of the family, was arrested. She was murdered with her companions on 18 July 1918, aged 53, by being thrown into a deep mining pit. A hand grenade was thrown in but only one person died. Singing was heard from the pit and a second grenade was thrown in. Their remains were found several months later and historians believe that she died slowly, either from her injuries or starvation. She was initially buried in Beijing but later was reburied in Jerusalem. Elisabeth was canonised by the Russian Orthodox Church outside Russia in 1981 and in 1992 by the Moscow Patriarchate. Her convent has since been reopened in post-communist Russia.

Princess Irene

of Hesse and by Rhine

Born 11 July 1866 – died 11 November 1953

I am the third child of Grand Duke Louis IV of Hesse and by Rhine and Princess Alice. I was born at the end of the Austro-Prussian War (Seven Weeks' War) and my parents named me Irene, after Eirene, the Greek word for peace. My childhood was quite simple for royalty. We had an English nanny. Our mother often took us to visit hospital wards and charities, something we all developed an interest in, although my sister Ella (Elisabeth) was most like our mother.

In 1873 my brother Frittie died after falling out of a window. Five years later we all came down with diphtheria, during which I lost my mother and our youngest sister. After our mother died, we became close to our maternal grandmother, Queen Victoria and we would often visit her in England and in particular, at Osborne House on the Isle of Wight. My eldest sister, Victoria, became a mother figure to all of us after our mother died.

When I was 22, I married my first cousin, Prince Henry of Prussia. He was the son of Princess Victoria, my mother's

eldest sister. I went to live in Berlin, Prussia. It was a happy marriage, although the wedding ceremony itself was not held in happy circumstances as it took place when Henry's father was dying from throat cancer.

We had three boys: Waldemar, Sigismund and Henry. The two eldest were named after my husband's two brothers, who had died in childhood. Sadly, both Waldemar and Henry had haemophilia. It was very difficult to prevent young children from having minor bumps and Henry died when he was only four after hitting his head. I was heartbroken. Waldemar managed to live until the age of 56, which is a good age for a haemophiliac, although, of course, it is still difficult to see your son die before you. Fortunately, Sigismund didn't have it. He married Princess Charlotte of Saxe-Altenburg and they have two children, Barbara and Alfred. They moved to Costa Rica in 1927 and I don't see much of them now.

My husband Henry served in the German Navy and during the First World War he was the Commander-in-Chief of the Baltic Fleet. Following the abdication of all the German Royal Families after the war, we became private citizens and now live on our estate in northern Germany.

In the early 1920s an imposter appeared, claiming to be my niece Anastasia, who along with her siblings and parents Tsar Nicholas II and my sister Alix were murdered by the Bolsheviks during the Russian Revolution. The imposter claimed that she had escaped and survived. I went to meet her but I knew immediately it wasn't Anastasia. Although I hadn't seen Anastasia for nine years, her facial features were so different that

I knew at once she was an imposter. I think the girl must have been mentally unstable. However, this episode really upset me. Olga, Nicholas's sister, also met her and was also unconvinced by her. The Russian Revolution was so terrible, so many people died, including two of my sisters, four nieces and my nephew.

Henry died in 1929. I feel lonely now as my husband, siblings and two of my children have all died, and Sigismund and his children live in Costa Rica, and I only occasionally get to see my grandchildren.

Postscript: Irene died on 11 November 1953, aged 87. She left her estate to her grand-daughter, Barbara.

Grand Duke Ernest Louis

of Hesse and by Rhine

Born 25 November 1868 – died 9 October 1937

In German, my name is Ernst Ludwig. I am the fourth child and oldest son of Grand Duke Louis IV of Hesse and by Rhine and Princess Alice. My education was very similar to my sisters, except that I went to university in Leipzig and then to the University of Giessen, where I studied history, literature, art and politics. Afterwards I served for a while in the Prussian Army, although I did not particularly enjoy the military.

When I was five, my only brother, Frittie, died. We had been playing a game together and he fell out of a window. He was only two and he had haemophilia. We will never know whether he would have died anyway, as he fell 20 feet, but obviously with haemophilia there was no way he could have survived. I was so devastated, I even had a dream that I had gone up to heaven and asked God to let me have Frittie again and he came to me and took my hand. I blame myself for Frittie's death; I feel I should have been able to prevent it. His death is something I will never forget.

At the age of 10, my family and I fell ill with diphtheria and my mother and my little sister, May, died. That was also devastating and I remember saying that I wish we could all die together and not alone like poor Frittie.

In 1892 my father died and I became the Grand Duke, at the age of 24. Hesse and by Rhine is a very small principality, of which I became the head of state.

Two years later, in 1894, I married my first cousin, Princess Victoria Melita of Saxe-Coburg and Gotha. She was my Uncle Alfred's daughter and was known as Ducky. It was arranged by our family. I didn't particularly want to marry her – or anyone for that matter – but I knew that it was very much expected of me to marry and have children in order to secure the succession. She was a very sociable person, which should have been a good thing for a Grand Duchess, but unfortunately she had no sense of responsibility and didn't take her duties very seriously. So she was not very supportive of me in my role as the Grand Duke. We had one child, Elizabeth, whom I loved very much. Later Ducky had a stillbirth in 1900.

At the beginning of our marriage we tried to make it work but eventually we ended up leading separate lives. She spent a lot of time gambling in the south of France and we finally got divorced in 1901, after Grandmama's (Queen Victoria) death. I think she would have been horrified if she knew of our divorce, especially as she had been involved in arranging our marriage and we were both her grandchildren.

Ducky and I shared custody of Elizabeth. Once I found Elizabeth crying when she was due to go back to her mother and she said to me, "Mama says she loves me but you really do love me". Sadly, she died of typhoid in 1903, when she was only eight. We were spending time with my sister Alix and her family in Poland and she contracted the illness and died very quickly. I sent a telegram to Ducky but she didn't arrive in time. That was the worst thing that has ever happened to me, worse even than losing my mother or Frittie. Elizabeth was my whole world; losing her was very hard and I still think of her and miss her after all these years.

I married a second time in 1905 as I still needed an heir. My second wife is Princess Eleonore of Solms-Hohensolms-Lich. I get on much better with her than Ducky. We had two sons, George and Louis. My interests are literature and the arts. I was a patron to artists and writers and I enjoyed meeting intellectuals. I helped create artists' colonies. I am an author of essays, plays and piano compositions.

During the Great War, the people of Darmstadt suffered like the rest of Germany with hunger and loss of life. I served in the Army at the Emperor's headquarters (my cousin Wilhelm was the Emperor at the time). I left Eleonore in Hesse serving as Regent. After the war ended, I was forced to abdicate, along with the other German royals, and I became a private citizen. However, we were able to continue living in Darmstadt. The

German people were angry with Wilhelm and he was forced to live in exile in the Netherlands but the rest of us were able to stay in Germany. Since then, I have really just been living in retirement. I was so sad to learn that my sisters Alix and Ella, who had both married into the Russian Royal Family, were murdered by the Bolsheviks in the Russian Revolution. I have remained close to my other siblings, even though we live in different countries.

My eldest son George is married to Cecile of Greece, who is technically a Princess, and they have three children. My son Louis will soon marry an English woman who is not royal, but that doesn't matter anymore as we are not royals now.

Postscript: Ernest died in October 1937 after a long illness, aged 68. He was given a large ceremonial funeral as he was still popular with the people of Darmstadt. He was buried next to his beloved daughter Elizabeth. In November 1937 Eleonore, George and Cecile and their two eldest children were travelling by plane to England to attend Louis' wedding when Cecile went into labour and gave birth. The pilot tried to land the plane but they crashed during a storm and they all died. Louis adopted George's youngest child, Johanna, who had been orphaned by the plane crash. However, she died just two years later in 1939 from meningitis. Louis had no children of his own and he died in 1968, aged 59.

It is believed that Ernest was gay. His first wife, Victoria Melita, told her relatives that she had found him in bed with a man, a stable-boy, although she did not make it public at the time. He also had a long-term relationship with Karl August Lingner.

Prince Friedrich
of Hesse and by Rhine

Born 7 October 1870 – died 29 May 1873

Postscript: *Known as Frittie, he was the fifth child of Grand Duke Louis IV of Hesse and by Rhine and Princess Alice. His haemophilia was first discovered at the age of two when he cut his ear and bled for three days. He was a cheerful and lively boy. In May 1873 he and his brother Ernest were playing together in their mother's bedroom. Ernest ran to another room and Frittie got on a chair to look through the window in order to see him but the chair tipped and Frittie fell out of the window 20 feet to the ground. He initially survived the fall but slipped into unconsciousness and died only hours later aged just two. It is not known whether he would have died anyway, but as his initial injuries did not appear serious it is believed that the haemophilia certainly contributed to his death.*

Empress Alexandra Feodorovna
of Russia

Born 6 June 1872 – died 17 July 1918

I was born Princess Alix of Hesse and by Rhine and my parents were the Grand Duke Louis IV of Hesse and by Rhine and Princess Alice. My first years of childhood were happy. My older brother Frittie died in 1873 but I was too young to remember him. However, when I was six, diphtheria swept through our family and my mother and younger sister May died. My family told me that I became shy and withdrawn after I lost my mother. I was close to all my siblings but especially to Ernest, who I was closest to in age. My eldest sister, Victoria, did her best to mother us but she left to marry and live in England when I was still only 12. Ella (Elisabeth) also got married that same year and went to live in Russia. Irene married when I was 16 and moved to Berlin.

I met Nicholas, who later became Tsar Nicholas II of Russia, at Ella's wedding and we saw each other a number of times after that. However, my family had initially wanted me to marry Prince Eddy (Prince Albert Victor, Duke of Clarence and

Avondale, the son of Edward VII) but I did not love him in a romantic way as I already liked Nicky. Nicky's family wanted him to marry Princess Hélène d'Orleans or my cousin, Princess Margaret of Prussia, but neither of those matches worked out. However, I was concerned that I would have to change my religion to Russian Orthodoxy. It was not easy for me to change my religion, nevertheless as I learnt more about Russian Orthodoxy, and with my sister Ella's encouragement, I was able to convert with a clear conscience.

Nicky and I are second cousins as we have the same great-grandmother, Princess Wilhelmine of Baden, my father's grandmother. We were married in the chapel of the Winter Palace in St Petersburg in November 1894, very shortly after Nicky had become Tsar. His father had died at the age of 49, and although I knew Nicky would be Tsar one day, I hadn't expected it to be so soon and to start our married life as Tsar and Tsarina. His father died on 1 November and was buried on 19 November and the wedding was held on 26 November. There was criticism from the public and from some family members that our wedding was held so soon but it was actually a sombre occasion.

I remember during the coronation festivities, in what should have been a happy occasion, many poor people were trampled to death when the crowd rushed forward for gifts of food and commemorative mugs. It was a terrible tragedy and some even said it was a bad omen for Nicky as Tsar.

Obviously, my life changed a great deal from being a Princess in a small principality in Germany to becoming the Tsarina of Russia. I found it overwhelming because I am a very shy person by nature so I don't really enjoy public events. I do speak French, so that meant communicating at the Russian Court was easy for me because everyone speaks French rather than Russian.

We have had a happy marriage and have five children: four girls and a boy. Olga was born one year after our wedding and Alexei, the youngest, was born in 1904, nine years later. I call him Sunbeam as he really is my pride and joy. It was important to have a son as girls are only allowed to become Empress of Russia in their own right if there are no living male relatives at all.

Unfortunately, Alexei has haemophilia. Our doctor diagnosed this shortly after he was born; he noticed that his cuts and bruises were slow to heal. It was terrible to know that he could die from a relatively minor injury, like my brother Frittie did, and this has made me terribly anxious for him all the time. I felt guilty knowing that I have probably passed the condition on to him, even though I don't suffer from it myself. We tried to prevent accidents from happening to him by being very strict about what he could do. The haemophilia has caused him a lot of physical pain, which has been very hard to watch as a mother. We kept his condition secret for a long time because we did not want people to hold it against him or to see the next Tsar as a weak man who could bleed to death following a very minor injury. I did tell my sisters but initially we didn't even tell my mother-in-law.

I get on well with most of Nicky's family, including his sisters Xenia and Olga but not with my mother-in-law. We were worried that she would turn the whole Russian Court against me if she knew about Alexei's condition. She wants to be the most important person in all her sons' lives. At Russian state occasions, the Tsar's mother takes precedence over his wife, which is something I can cope with, but I should be and am the most important person in Nicky's life in all our private matters. We lived in the Alexander Palace, just outside St Petersburg, because we wanted a quiet family life, but in hindsight maybe we were a bit too cut off from the rest of the family.

None of the doctors could help Alexei with his condition. Eventually, I met Rasputin, a holy man from Siberia, who prayed for him and his condition improved. Rasputin was our friend and confidante and he gave us advice. However, some of our relatives and members of the Russian Court did not like him at all. They thought he was influencing Nicky in matters of state. In 1912 I eventually told Nicky's mother and sisters about Alexei's haemophilia but, as I feared, it did backfire. They didn't keep it to themselves and I was hated even more because I was blamed for giving it to him. They called it the "English disease". During that year, we were visiting Spala in Russian Poland when Alexei had a severe attack of haemophilia and he nearly died. It was terrifying. He was even given the last rites but then Rasputin telegrammed us saying that Alexei would get better and not to let the doctors bother him too much. After that, he miraculously recovered and came back from the brink of death. That episode cemented my absolute faith in Rasputin, and my faith in God became a lot stronger.

Fortunately, our girls are all healthy but I suffer from sciatica, which gives me pain in my legs. I also have an enlarged heart and have migraines and sometimes on bad days I am confined to a wheelchair. I think it is possible that the worry about Alexei makes my condition worse. I am not able to be very pro-active and I am constantly tired, although sleep is a struggle for me. It meant that I couldn't be around for my children as much as I would have liked.

Nicky and I made the decision that our daughters would be able to marry for love providing they wanted to marry royals. We knew that Prince Alexander of Serbia was fond of Tatiana, our second eldest daughter. We went to Romania in the summer of 1914 because we were considering Olga marrying the Crown Prince of Romania but that didn't work out. But then the war broke out and all thoughts of marrying our daughters were put on hold.

Nicky was often busy as head of state and government, which ruled over the vast empire of Russia. As time went by, the situation became unsettled due to the revolutionaries stirring up trouble with their ideologies. Being of German birth, the war with Germany made things very difficult for me, and it gave the Russian people an excuse to hate me even more. It meant that my family were separated by the war as Ella and I live in Russia, Irene and Ernie live in Germany and Victoria is in England.

Our friend Rasputin advised that Nicky should go and lead the Army from the front in 1915. He was sometimes away for long periods but it was the right thing to do as he replaced his cousin Nikolasha, who had been leading the Army. That man was so arrogant; he was behaving as if he was Tsar himself. While Nicky was away at the front, I acted as Regent and I was the first Empress of Russia to receive government ministers since Catherine the Great in 1796. I found that difficult because the ministers were self-serving and did not care about the country. However, Rasputin helped me by giving advice.

The war went very badly for Russia, as many soldiers were killed and the people were short of food. Some family members even supported a coup d'état against Nicky although, fortunately, it failed because we found out about it in time. They wanted to depose Nicky, the rightful Tsar, and get Kirill Vladimirovich to act as Regent for Alexei until he became of age. Kirill was Victoria Melita's husband, who had previously divorced my brother Ernie. Even my mother-in-law was involved in this and she was sent to Kiev as a result. They also wanted to imprison me in a convent. So relationships with the family became very difficult.

People were so full of hatred for Rasputin that they made up the most vicious rumours about us, that he had sexual relationships with me and my daughters. It was quite awful. Even my sister Ella, came to see me to try and persuade me to get rid of him but I refused to do so. A short time later, he was murdered by Felix Yusupov (my niece's husband), Dimitri Pavlovich (Nicky's cousin) and the right-wing politician Vladimir Purishkevich. It was deeply shocking that they should betray us like this; they murdered him in cold blood. Some family members had the audacity to ask Nicky for leniency for them. They were all sent to the front by Nicky, but I thought that was a very light punishment for such a serious crime.

The Great War placed a massive burden on the government and the economy. There were mass shortages and hunger. A few months later, in early 1917, the Revolution happened. The workers went on strike and began rioting. Nicky ordered the Army to restore order and they fired into the crowd. He dissolved the Duma (the Russian Parliament) but the next day the soldiers began supporting the mob. Nicky tried to get back to St Petersburg but whilst stuck on the train his generals strongly advised him to abdicate, which he did. He realised that his position had become untenable. That ended 1,000 years of monarchy in Russia. We were all in utter shock that this could have happened – it felt like the end of the world.

We became prisoners in our own palace and were surrounded by guards. We decided it would be best to leave Russia and tried to make plans. The British government initially agreed for us to go there but our children all got measles and we couldn't leave. By the time they had all recovered, the British government withdrew their offer. A few months later, we were moved to Tobolsk in Siberia, where we were kept under house arrest in the Governor's mansion. We had wanted to go to our summer residence in Crimea but were told it was too dangerous to travel there because there was rioting and the upper classes were being attacked and their homes burnt. We still hoped we would be rescued by the White Russians and helped to go abroad. The Bolsheviks seized power in the October Revolution of 1917 and they moved us to Yekaterinburg, where conditions became worse. I spent my time reading the Bible or playing cards with the children.

I have had time to reflect and I wonder whether we shouldn't have lived such a secluded life away from the family and taken more advice from them. If we had, then maybe we would have kept them on side with us. Personally, I don't think Russia should have joined the war. Maybe the Revolution would never have happened if it wasn't for the war.

Postscript: On the night of 17 July 1918, the family were gathered in the cellar and were murdered. Nicholas was shot first and died instantly. The girls took longer to die as they had sewn jewels into their undergarments which deflected the bullets, so finally they were shot in the head. Alexei was the last to die, having played dead, but he was also shot. Even the family dog was shot dead. Their bodies were thrown down a mine shaft. Decades later, their bodies were found and were confirmed by DNA tests. In 1998, after the fall of communism, a funeral service was finally held and they were buried in St Peter and Paul Cathedral in St Petersburg. In 1981 the family were canonised by the Russian Orthodox Church outside of Russia and in 2000 they were canonised by the Church within Russia.

After their deaths the house where they were imprisoned in Yekaterinburg became a museum but it was demolished because it attracted many people sympathetic to the royal family. Later a church was built on the site known as "the Church on Blood", which has become a shrine to the family.

Princess Marie

of Hesse and by Rhine

Born 24 May 1874 – died 16 November 1878

Postscript: *Known to her family as May, she was the youngest child of Grand Duke Louis IV of Hesse and by Rhine and Princess Alice. She was born a year after her brother, Frittie, had died after falling from a window. Alice thought that she bore a strong resemblance to him. She was closest in age to her sister Alix. In November 1878, all the family contracted diphtheria. Marie died from the illness on 16 November, aged just four. Her mother Alice died a month later.*

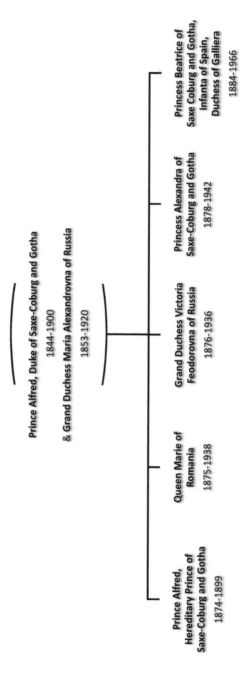

Family Tree of Prince Alfred

Fourth Child of Queen Victoria

Prince Alfred, Duke of Saxe-Coburg and Gotha
1844-1900
& Grand Duchess Maria Alexandrovna of Russia
1853-1920

Prince Alfred,
Hereditary Prince of
Saxe-Coburg and Gotha
1874-1899

Queen Marie of
Romania
1875-1938

Grand Duchess Victoria
Feodorovna of Russia
1876-1936

Princess Alexandra of
Saxe-Coburg and Gotha
1878-1942

Princess Beatrice of
Saxe Coburg and Gotha,
Infanta of Spain,
Duchess of Galliera
1884-1966

Prince Alfred

Duke of Saxe-Coburg and Gotha

Born 6 August 1844 – died 31 July 1900

I am the fourth child of Queen Victoria and Prince Albert. I was 17 when my father died. Apart from that, I think I had an easier childhood than my older brother, Bertie, who was heir to the throne. There was less pressure on me and more freedom to make my own decisions. I joined the Royal Navy when I was 14 in 1858, which is something I wanted to do ever since I was a little boy. I didn't need to go to university like my brother as I was unlikely ever to be King.

I saw a lot of the world with the Navy and as part of my royal duties. I was often away for months at a time. I went to the Cape Colony (South Africa) and Australia twice, which took months to travel there and back by sea. I was the first member of the Royal Family to visit Australia. On my second visit, in 1868, I was in Sydney when I was shot in the back just to the right of my spine. I was very lucky and I recovered. A hospital was even named after me. They caught the man – his name was Henry James O'Farrell. It seems he was a Catholic and an anti-royalist.

They wanted to execute him and I tried to intercede for him because I believe in Christian forgiveness and also because I believed he was mentally ill, but they hanged him regardless. Fortunately, that was the only assassination attempt on my life but my mother has had eight attempts on hers. It seems to be par for the course for monarchs and political leaders in general.

I got married when I was 30 to Grand Duchess Maria Alexandrovna of Russia, the daughter of Tsar Alexander II. We don't spend that much time together. We married for love but over time our feelings for each other have cooled. She says I have a drinking problem, which I probably do, and I have had a few affairs, although a lot less than my brother Bertie. Maria and I have very different interests. She likes literature and theatre, which I find boring, whereas I like hunting and politics. We tend to have different social lives but she does accompany me on royal duties. When we got married, a small English bakery commemorated our wedding and named the Marie biscuit after her.

My Uncle Ernest was Duke of Saxe-Coburg and Gotha and as he had no children I was expected at some point to become Duke. It should have passed to Bertie, my older brother, but he renounced his right to the throne just before he got married because he was heir to the British throne anyway. So I have known for a long time that I would eventually become Duke, which I did in 1893. We moved to Saxe-Coburg in 1889 because my uncle was getting older and his health was deteriorating. It was a difficult move for me as it is a small, land-locked country and I obviously like the sea. At first the people did not really like me, as I was seen as a foreigner, but over time they seemed to have warmed to me. When I was a lot younger, back in 1862, the Greek people suggested that I become King of Greece. They had overthrown their own King Otto. Sometimes I wonder what would have happened if I had become King of Greece but I am glad that didn't happen, as the Greek crown was not something I particularly wanted.

We had five children: one son and four daughters. My son Alfred died last year in a tragic accident. He had consumption and there have been lots of rumours about his death. Some people said he had a tumour but most people think he shot himself. He was sent to a sanatorium in Austria and died of his wounds there. It was a great shock to us and he was only 24. There were also rumours that he had a secret marriage but I certainly don't know about that. He was expected to inherit my throne one day but clearly, that won't happen now. Daughters can't rule here, so it will pass to a male relative, but we are not sure who yet.

My three eldest daughters are all married. Missy (Marie) is married to Crown Prince Ferdinand of Romania, Ducky (Victoria Melita) is married to her cousin Ernest, the Grand Duke of Hesse and by Rhine, and Sandra (Alexandra) is married to another Prince Ernest. So only my youngest, Beatrice, is unmarried. I am a little worried about Ducky because she seems to be quite unhappily married to Ernest. My wife arranged all their marriages.

We both keep in touch with our families. Maria goes back to Russia and once when she was there for her father's silver jubilee, they narrowly escaped a terrorist attack. A bomb exploded at the Winter Palace but fortunately they were all unharmed.

Postscript: Alfred died on 30 July 1900 of throat cancer, aged 55. He was succeeded by his nephew, Prince Charles Edward (Prince Leopold's son).

Prince Alfred

Born 15 October 1874 – died 6 February 1899

I am the son of Prince Alfred, Duke of Saxe-Coburg and Gotha, and Grand Duchess Maria Alexandrovna of Russia. My father became the Duke of Saxe-Coburg and Gotha in 1893 after the death of my great uncle Ernest, who had no children. However, at the time of my birth at Buckingham Palace, my father was the Duke of Edinburgh.

I spent most of my childhood in England at Clarence House and we also had an estate in the country at Eastwell Park, Surrey. My father was in the Navy, so he was often away. I have four younger sisters. I was tutored at home initially but later sent to Germany to complete my education, as I am expected one day to become Duke of Saxe-Coburg. I attended a military academy and I joined the Army. My mother made all the decisions regarding my education. She took us to Russia many times to visit our Russian relatives. She was Tsar Alexander II's daughter but now her nephew, Nicholas II, is the current Tsar.

The rest of my family moved to Germany after me in 1889

so that my father could learn the ropes before becoming Duke himself. Now I am first in line to the throne.

In 1895 I was due to marry Duchess Elsa Matilda Marie from Württemberg but the marriage never happened. I can't say that I'm sorry because I do not want to settle down at the moment. I like spending time with my friends and have lots of girlfriends. I am still in the Army but I don't really enjoy the military life. I hate how regimented and strict it is, although being a Prince I am expected to serve in the military for a few years at least. I am still not that close to my father, as I find him quite emotionally distant, even though he is around more now that he has become the Duke.

Postscript: During his parents' silver wedding anniversary, Alfred shot himself, and against doctor's orders he was taken to a sanatorium in Austria. He died two weeks later from his injuries, aged 24. Historians now believe that Alfred had a sexually transmitted disease. It is not clear exactly why he shot himself. There were many rumours, including that he had a secret marriage, but there is no evidence for that. In her memoirs, his sister Marie simply stated that "his health broke down". Others said that he died of consumption but the accepted view is that he shot himself.

At his funeral his mother broke down uncontrollably and sank to her knees, crossing herself many times. His father blamed her for Alfred's death, as she had been responsible for his education. Alfred's sisters were unable to succeed the throne as women were not allowed to reign in their own right in any of the German principalities. A year later Alfred's father also died and he was succeeded by Charles Edward, Prince Leopold's son.

Queen Marie

of Romania

Born 29 October 1875 – died 18 July 1938

My parents were Prince Alfred, Duke of Saxe-Coburg and Gotha, and Grand Duchess Maria Alexandrovna of Russia. I was their second child. I had an older brother and three younger sisters. I spent my early years in England. Our father was largely absent, as he was in the Navy, but my mother was an important person in our lives and we probably saw our mother more than most upper-class children. However, she was a believer in separating the generations, so there was some formality between us, and even as adults we never talked as though we were equals. I was closest to my sister Victoria Melita, known as Ducky.

We moved to Saxe-Coburg in 1889, a few years before my father succeeded my great uncle Ernest as Duke. Even after we moved there, we didn't see him that often because he was always travelling somewhere. I was sad to leave England but excited for my new life in Germany. I already spoke German because my father was English-German and my mother was Russian-

German. Now I speak four languages: English, German, French and Romanian.

I remember when I was about 17 they wanted me to marry my cousin, George (George V). When I say they, I mean my father, George's father and Grandmamma (Queen Victoria). However, our mothers were not happy about it, mainly because they didn't like each other. Also, my mother was disapproving of first cousins marrying, as it was forbidden in the Russian Orthodox Church. I was fond of him and loved him as a cousin, but I didn't want to marry him.

After that episode, my mother arranged my marriage to Crown Prince Ferdinand of Romania. We first met at a gala dinner and I found him shy but pleasant. He was 10 years older than me and we were married on 10 January 1893 in Germany. We went to live in Romania and the first years of our marriage were not that easy because we barely knew each other. We had to learn how to live together but we gradually came to understand each other and although we never really in love, we did love each other in a familial way.

As the Romanian Royal Family were essentially German they conversed in German, which was easy for me as I could already speak the language. So it was not necessary for me to learn Romanian, but I chose to learn it as I wanted to learn about Romania and understand the people more. I accompanied my husband on royal duties, which I enjoyed, as I like meeting new people. Despite this, it took me some time to become accustomed to living in Romania, as I was very homesick. I missed my family and I was living in a different country where I didn't know anyone. Nevertheless, over time I have grown to love Romania.

Nine months after our marriage, I gave birth to my first child, Prince Carol. The very next year I had Elizabeth. I was not able to raise my two eldest children, as they were taken from me and brought up by King Carol I and Queen Elizabeth, who were my husband's uncle and aunt. They were childless, having lost a young daughter, and were desperate to have their own children, so they took mine. We had no say in this as Carol was a tyrant, but as you can imagine this was very hard for me. I felt very resentful towards them. My husband wasn't able to stand up to Carol. We did see the children and they knew that I was their real mother but we were unable to have much of an influence on their lives. Both of them were spoilt rotten and they have not turned out that well. Carol, my son, is something of a playboy and Elizabeth, too, seems to think only of herself.

After a few years, I went on to have four more children, all of whom I did raise myself: Maria, Nicholas, Ileana and Mircea. However, Mircea, my youngest son, died at three years of age from pneumonia, which was devastating.

In 1900, the year Maria was born, my brother Alfred died suddenly at the age of 24. His health broke down during my parents' silver wedding anniversary celebrations. My mother broke down, crying uncontrollably, at his funeral. Shortly after that my father and grandmother, Queen Victoria, also died, so it was a very sad time.

Ferdinand ascended the throne in 1914, when I was 39 and he was 49. Our lives changed quite a bit then but because of the Great War the coronation was delayed until 1922. In 1916 Romania entered the Great War on the side of the allies. Romania made great sacrifices and lost a lot of men. I identified more with the English side of my family than the German side, so I was at least relieved that we were fighting on the allied side. At the end of the war, the Romanian delegation, led by the Prime Minister, were not able to negotiate a good deal for Romania at the Paris Peace Conference. I went there instead and was immediately welcomed by Georges Clemenceau, the French Prime Minister, and I successfully achieved a much better post-war deal. As a result, Romania's borders were expanded by 295,000 square kilometres, increasing the population by 10 million people.

Carol married a woman called Zizi Lambrino, who was not royal, but their marriage was later annulled. Then he married Princess Helen of Greece and they had a son, Michael. I thought he was finally settling down but then he became involved with a mistress named Magda Lupescu. He left Helen and Michael and renounced his parental rights. He refused to accept advice to take Helen back. The scandal that ensued forced him to renounce his right to the throne. He left Romania and went abroad with Magda.

In 1926 I visited the USA with my children Nicholas and Ileana. I was welcomed enthusiastically by the people there and visited the White House. I always wanted to go back but I never did.

Ferdinand died in 1927 from cancer at the age of 61 and things have been difficult since then. He was succeeded by our grandson, Michael, who was only five years old at the time. As he was too young to rule, a regency council was set up, consisting of my son Nicholas, Michael's mother Helen and the Patriarch of the Romanian Orthodox Church. However, in 1930 Carol decided that he did want to be King and he managed to overthrow his own son. This we could have accepted but he also brought Magda back with him, who I find to be a truly vile woman. I understand that men have mistresses and I am not priggish in any sense of the word but I cannot accept the way he lives so openly with her and I find her quite selfish and arrogant. She drains the Romanian treasury to fund herself and her friends, not caring about how the Romanian people are impoverished.

The Great Depression has also hit Romania hard and the people hate her because of her opulent lifestyle while they are starving. Carol also took back custody of Michael but he refused to have Helen back. In fact she was exiled from Romania and Michael was only allowed to visit her in summertime.

My daughter Elizabeth married the Crown Prince of Greece, Prince George, but they divorced in 1935. She didn't have any children. Maria married King Alexander of Yugoslavia and she has three boys. Her eldest, Peter, is now King of Yugoslavia. Nicholas married a non-royal woman in 1930, so Carol stripped him of his royal titles and banished him from Romania, which seems quite hypocritical since Carol's first wife was not royal and nor is his mistress Magda. Nicholas doesn't have any children. Ileana, my sweet daughter, was very affectionate towards me. In 1931 Carol forced her to marry Archduke Anton of Austria and then banished her from Romania too because I think he was jealous of her popularity. I often visit her and her children in Austria but she rarely receives permission to visit me here. I also visit Belgrade to see Maria and her children.

Recently I have not been well. I went to a sanatorium in Italy and have now transferred to one in Dresden, Germany, but I think I am near my end, so I want to go back to Romania to die there. I asked Carol if I could come back by aeroplane but he turned me down. Even Hitler offered me a medical flight but I did not want to take up his offer, so in the end I travelled back by train.

Postscript: Marie died of pancreatic cancer on 18 July 1938, aged 62. At her deathbed were Carol, Elizabeth and her grandson, Michael. She was the last Queen of Romania, as Carol was not married during his 10-year reign and Michael was not married during his reign.

Carol reigned until 1940, when he was deposed by the military supported by the people. Michael succeeded him and became King for a second time at the age of 18. Officially, he reigned in his own right as he was of age, but unofficially his mother Helen was the power behind the throne. However, the Romanian government was led by the military dictator Ion Antonescu, who was allied with the Nazis. There was a coup in 1944 against him, supported by Michael, Helen and others. At that point, Romania joined the allies and declared war on Germany. After the Second World War the communists took control of Romania and in December 1947 Michael was forced to abdicate.

It is known that Marie was very depressed after the birth of her eldest two children, although historians are unsure whether this was caused by postnatal depression or because they were taken away to live with their uncle and aunt.

Marie was rumoured to have been romantically linked to several men throughout her marriage. In 1897 she became pregnant as a result of an affair and gave birth to a child in Coburg. It is not known whether the child was stillborn or whether it was sent to an orphanage. Lieutenant Gheorghe Cantacuzune is thought most likely to have been the child's father. There was also some speculation that her daughter Maria may have also been fathered by him. Historians also question Ileana's paternity and they also generally agree that Mircea was not Ferdinand's son. Her husband also had affairs during the marriage, although that was deemed acceptable for a man of his position.

Grand Duchess Victoria Feodorovna
of Russia

Born 25 November 1876 – died 1 March 1936

My parents were Prince Alfred, Duke of Saxe-Coburg and Gotha, and Grand Duchess Maria Alexandrovna of Russia. I was born Princess Victoria Melita of Edinburgh, as my father was Duke of Edinburgh at the time. My father, who was in the Navy, was stationed in Malta, so they named me Victoria Melita (for Malta) but I am known as Ducky to my family and friends. I was the middle child. I had two older siblings, Affie and Missy (Alfred and Marie) and two younger siblings, Sandra (Alexandra) and Beatrice.

I was brought up mainly in England and then we moved to Coburg, Germany, in 1889, a few years before my father succeeded the Ducal throne in 1893. I could already speak German before we moved there. Growing up, I was closest to my sister Missy. She got married to Crown Prince Ferdinand of Romania and we took the separation very hard. I was then paired up with my paternal cousin, Ernest Louis, Grand Duke of Hesse and by Rhine. Our family were keen for us to marry, which we did on 19 April 1894 in Coburg. I liked him, so I didn't resist the marriage, but I was not in love with him. We had a daughter, Elisabeth, and I also had a stillborn son in 1900, which left me grief-stricken and desperately sad for quite a while, especially as my brother and father died all within a year.

However, it turned out not to be a happy marriage, as we were very incompatible. We had very different personalities and I was upset by Ernie's lack of affection towards me. I found out that Ernie slept with men; stable-hands and kitchen help. I didn't make that public at the time because it would have been scandalous but I felt trapped in an unhappy and loveless marriage. I started thinking about divorce but my grandmother, Queen Victoria, refused to sanction it. We tried to live separately and shared the upbringing of Elisabeth, but I wanted to live my life without being tied to Ernie. Eventually, after Queen Victoria died, I was able to initiate divorce proceedings against Ernie and our marriage was dissolved by the Supreme Court of Hesse in 1901. I went back to live with my mother in Coburg. The divorce was a huge scandal at the time and for a while I was not welcome on the social scene at all, so it was a very difficult time for me. I also felt that Elisabeth blamed me for the divorce, even though we shared custody of her, but I had left the family home. Now I have had other children, I know that I spoilt her terribly in trying to reconnect with her.

Then, sadly, Elisabeth died at the age of eight from typhoid in 1903. That was the worst thing ever to happen to me – it was heartbreaking. I received a telegram informing me that she was seriously ill but before I arrived I received a second telegram saying she had died, so I didn't get to say goodbye. That haunts me to this day.

I remember when I first noticed my cousin, Kirill Vladimirovich; it was in 1891 when we travelled to the funeral of one of our relatives in Russia. He was very handsome and we were attracted to each other. After my divorce, I became closer to Kirill, but there was a lot of opposition to us marrying. I was tainted by my divorce and the Russian Orthodox Church forbade the marriage of first cousins.

During the war between Russia and Japan in 1905, Kirill's ship was blown up and he was one of the few survivors. Following that experience, he told me that he became determined to marry me despite the opposition. So we married later that year. My mother's chaplain agreed to marry us, even though he was Russian Orthodox. It was a very small wedding. When Tsar Nicholas II heard of the marriage, Kirill was stripped of his titles (Grand Duke of Russia) and banished from Russia. We moved to Paris, which I enjoyed, and as I already spoke French the language wasn't a problem. However, it was harder for Kirill because he not only had to leave Russia but he also was no longer able to serve in the Russian Navy, which he loved. I did feel a bit guilty at first that marrying me had caused him so many problems but he assured me it was a sacrifice he was willing to make for love.

I felt I matured quite a bit as I entered my thirties and one of the things I did was to convert to the Russian Orthodox Church, which pleased Kirill and my mother. I gave birth to our first child, whom we named Maria after both her grandmothers, and then I had another daughter, Kira, in 1909. Nicky (the Tsar) allowed us to move back to Russia that year and restored Kirill's titles to him and I became Grand Duchess. At that point, Kirill's father had just died and so Kirill became third in line to the throne, after Nicky's son, Alexei, and Nicky's brother, Misha.

We lived in St Petersburg. Kirill re-joined the Navy and I very much enjoyed entertaining and being part of Russia's high society. By that time, I was accepted as Kirill's wife, now that we had been forgiven by the Tsar. I have learnt a bit of Russian but am not very fluent. French was frequently spoken in aristocratic circles, so Russian was not so important. I never became that close to Nicky and Alix (Empress Alexandra) but had a relatively good relationship with the rest of the family. The most difficult part of living in Russia was the long winter. I used to visit Missy in Romania and my mother in Coburg and also the south of France, where she had a house. Altogether I was much happier than I was before. We spent summers on our yacht and were in Riga when the Great War broke out.

During the war, I worked as a Red Cross nurse and also organised an ambulance unit on the Eastern Front. Sometimes I even carried out my duties under enemy fire. It meant that I wasn't that far from Kirill, as he was in the Navy. We shared the rest of the family's concern over the relationship between Nicky, Alix and Rasputin, as he seemed to be exerting more and more influence over them. We were worried that he was taking advantage of their daughters. Their nanny told us that he was allowed to enter the nursery and he would sit caressing the girls. We also felt that their relationship with him was hugely damaging the prestige of the monarchy. Rasputin was assassinated in 1916 by Felix Yusupov, Dimitri Pavlovich and others. Kirill and I signed a letter asking Nicky to show leniency to Dimitri, our relative, but Nicky sent him to the front as punishment.

Nicky was forced to abdicate following the February Revolution in 1917. There was a lot of political turmoil and it felt like everything was breaking down. We lost our titles again. During that period, I discovered that I was pregnant at the age of 41, which made things particularly worrying. Kirill led his naval unit to the Provisional Government's headquarters and swore loyalty to them in an effort to restore order. Some people perceived that as treason but I supported Kirill. Nicky and Alix and their family were all under house arrest but we were still living freely in our own house. I sympathised with the people who wanted reform but things actually got worse. In the end we decided it would be best to leave Russia. It was an extremely difficult decision, especially for Kirill, as he was devoted to Russia.

Kirill and I and the girls left for Finland but we were unable to take much with us, so I sewed jewels into our clothing. I gave birth there to our son, Vladimir. It was an extremely difficult time as we ran out of supplies and had to beg for help from the family. Various members of our Russian family also left for different countries. I started to feel alienated from the English side of my family, as I don't think my cousin, George V, did enough to help the Russian Royal Family.

In 1919 we finally made it to Germany after the war had ended, where we were reunited with my mother. I hadn't seen her since before the war as we had been on opposing sides but she died the following year. Fortunately, she left her properties to me, which was a great help to us. My brother had already died and my older sister Missy didn't really need them, as she was Queen of Romania, so I was the next eldest child. We divided our time between our home in Coburg and our home in the south of France.

In 1923 Kirill suffered a nervous breakdown and I nursed him back to health. I think it was brought on by all the upheaval of having our lives turned upside down and Kirill felt he had lost his purpose in life.

I visited the USA in 1924 to try to raise support from America to help overthrow the Bolsheviks, who were now ruling Russia, or the USSR as it has become. But I did not get much support as America was going through an isolationist period.

My daughter Maria married the former German Prince Karl of Leiningen in 1925 and I always stayed with her when she gave birth to all her seven children. Kira is still unmarried and Vladimir too, as he is only 18. We have moved permanently to France and settled in St Briac in Brittany in order to spare the

German government any embarrassment after they established relations with Moscow. We don't have much money now and I sell some artwork to make an income.

I have a close bond with Vladimir, my only son. All my hopes for the future rest with him. I hired a tutor to educate him as I wanted to bring him up the way all Romanov Grand Dukes were brought up before the Revolution. After Tsar Nicholas, his son Alexei, and Nicholas' brother, Misha, were executed following the Revolution, Kirill is now the Tsar in exile, with Vladimir as the first in line. We lead a simple life now. Kirill plays golf and I have picnics and take part in the social life of the local community. We do see our relatives sometimes. Kirill's brothers live in Paris now and our other Russian relatives are settled in different countries. I still see my sisters Missy, Sandra and Beatrice. A few years ago, in 1933, I found my husband had been unfaithful to me, which was very upsetting after all we had been through and I felt betrayed, but I decided to carry on as normal for the sake of the children.

Postscript: Victoria Melita suffered a stroke in February 1936. Family and friends rushed to be at her bedside, including her sister Missy, but she died on 1 March 1936, aged 59. She was buried in the Ducal mausoleum in Coburg and in 1995 her remains were transferred to the Grand Ducal mausoleum in St Petersburg. Kirill was very lonely after her death and died two years later. Kira married Prince Louis Ferdinand of Prussia in 1938 just before Kirill died. Vladimir lived all his life in exile and was considered by some as the Tsar in exile. During the Second World War, he was sent to a concentration camp because he refused to issue a manifesto asking Russian émigrés to support Nazi Germany's war against the Soviet Union. In 1991 he was finally invited to visit St Petersburg by the Mayor, at the age of 74. He died one year later. His body was returned to Russia and was buried in St Petersburg.

Princess Alexandra

of Saxe-Coburg and Gotha

Born 1 September 1878 – died 16 April 1942

My parents were Prince Alfred, Duke of Saxe-Coburg and Gotha, and Grand Duchess Maria Alexandrovna of Russia. I am known as Sandra to my family and friends. I was born in Coburg during a family visit, although my early childhood was spent in England. At that point my father was Duke of Edinburgh, so we were minor British royals. In 1889 we moved to Coburg and in 1893 Great Uncle Ernest died and my father succeeded him as Duke of Saxe-Coburg and Gotha. My mother was thrilled to move to Germany because it meant she was away from her English relatives, particularly her mother-in-law, Queen Victoria, whom she didn't get on with, probably because they were both such headstrong people. We didn't see that much of my father as he was away for long periods serving in the Navy, which he missed when we moved there. Living in a tiny land-locked German state did not appeal to him.

When I was 17, I became engaged to Ernst, Prince of Hohenlohe-Langenburg, which was arranged by my mother. He was the grandson of Princess Feodora, Queen Victoria's half-sister. Ernst was 33, so was quite a bit older than me. I wasn't in love with him but I was so young I went along with what my mother wanted. We married the following year. Queen Victoria, my grandmother, was not happy about the marriage, as she said I was too young. My father wasn't particularly thrilled, as he

thought Ernst was a low-ranking royal, which was probably true. My mother also arranged my sisters' marriages but they all married higher ranking royals than me, perhaps because they were considered more beautiful. Missy married the Crown Prince of Romania, Ducky made two brilliant matches (the second time even as a divorced woman), and Beatrice married a Spanish prince.

In 1899 my brother Affie died suddenly, which was a huge shock, and my parents took it particularly very hard. My mother, who was usually so stoical, fell to her knees sobbing at his funeral. My father's health broke down shortly afterwards and he died the following year from a growth, but I also think it was from a broken heart after losing his only son. Queen Victoria died a year later in 1901.

We lived more like aristocrats than royals, although Ernst did become Regent of Coburg for about four years when my father died until my cousin, Charles Edward, became of age at 21. As my brother Affie had died, the succession moved to the next male heir, who was Charles Edward. It meant that we moved back to Coburg for that time and I was close to my mother. Ernst also held other roles, including being head of the Colonial Department of the Foreign Office in Germany in 1906. He also became vice-president of the Reichstag (parliament) in 1909-1910. On the death of his father, he was entitled to sit in the equivalent of the House of Lords in Wurttemberg until the November Revolution of 1918, when we became private citizens.

We had four children together: Gottfried, Marie Melita, Alexandra and Irma. Nine years later I gave birth to a baby boy, who only lived for two days, which was very sad.

Gottfried served in the German Army in the First World War. During the war, I worked as a Red Cross nurse like my sister Ducky (Victoria Melita) but she was on the Russian side and I was on the German side. My sister Missy (Marie) was also on the other side as Queen of Romania. It was a very strange and discomforting feeling to be on different sides from one's own sisters. Obviously, we didn't see each other during the war but at least we all survived it. I was particularly thankful that Ducky and her family managed to escape Russia, as so many of their relatives did not.

In 1918 Germany became a republic and we lost our titles and became private citizens. It didn't make a huge difference to our lives as we hadn't had high positions of status before. I imagine that those who were more important than us took it much harder, for example the former Kaiser and his family. My mother died in 1920 and we inherited her residence in the city. Ducky inherited her country residence, as they were virtually homeless, having escaped from Russia after the Revolution.

I have joined the Nazi Party and I support Hitler's endeavours, as Germany has suffered terrible repercussions after the end of the First World War. Gottfried is now fighting in the Army again during this war (Second World War) and I hope we will all survive again.

Postscript: Alexandra died on 16 April 1942, aged 63. She was survived by her husband, who died in 1950 at the age of 87. Gottfried was severely injured on the Russian Front and he was dismissed from the Army after the attempted assassination on Hitler's life in 1944. There was no suggestion that he was involved but Hitler had become very paranoid and dismissed many people from the Army for no apparent reason. Gottfried died in 1960, aged 63.

Princess Beatrice
Infanta of Spain, Duchess of Galliera
Born 20 April 1884 – died 13 July 1966

My parents were Prince Alfred, Duke of Saxe-Coburg and Gotha, and Grand Duchess Maria Alexandrovna of Russia. I was born in England and was their fifth and youngest child. I spent some of my very early years in Malta, where my father was stationed in the Navy, but we didn't see much of him growing up, as he was away carrying out his duties. We moved to Coburg when I was five and in 1893 my father succeeded my great uncle Ernest as the Duke of Saxe-Coburg and Gotha. My mother was domineering and I didn't see much of my brother Affie, as he was away at school, but I was close to my three sisters. However, Missy got married when I was only nine in 1893, the same year my father succeeded the Ducal throne. Ducky was married the following year and Sandra was married in 1896 when I was twelve. Affie died in 1899 and my father died the following year, so that left only my mother and me at home.

In 1902 I began a romance with my cousin, Grand Duke Michael Alexandrovich of Russia, Tsar Nicholas II's brother.

We fell in love but were prevented from marrying as the Russian Orthodox Church forbade the marriage of first cousins and Nicholas refused to grant an exception. Michael wrote to tell me that he couldn't marry me and I was heartbroken. I was sent to Egypt to recover from my heartbreak, which took a while, and I continued to

write to him. To make matters worse, my sister Ducky married Kirill Vladimirovich a couple of years later and he was also Russian Orthodox and a first cousin. However, they paid a heavy price because Kirill was stripped of his title and they were forced to live in exile for a few years. But at the time I thought it very hypocritical of Ducky because she had blamed Michael for the doomed romance, saying that we shouldn't have got involved in the first place.

I met my husband Alfonso (Infante of Spain, Duke of Galliera) when I attended my cousin Ena's (Victoria Eugenie) wedding to King Alfonso XIII of Spain in 1906. He was a cousin of King Alfonso. We married three years later, which was considered quite a long courtship in those days. Our wedding was held in Coburg and we had a Lutheran and a Catholic service, but I refused to convert to Catholicism, so my husband was stripped of his titles and we were exiled from Spain. That meant that we lived in Coburg. Alfonso said that he loved me so much that he didn't mind that we were exiled and he was also sure that we would be eventually allowed back to Spain. He was right and three years later his titles were restored and we moved to Spain. A year later I decided to convert to Catholicism, as

I became convinced that it was the true faith, which made Alfonso very happy. It might sound strange that I had refused to convert but I had been brought up in a very anti-Catholic environment, as my father was Lutheran and my mother was Russian Orthodox, but after we moved to Spain I was able to learn more about Catholicism and I changed my views.

We had three sons: Alvaro, Alonso and Ataulfo. Alvaro was born in Coburg and my other two sons were born in Madrid. As my husband is the King's cousin, we are considered to be minor royals. He was one of the first aviators in the Spanish Air Force and later became the Chief of Staff. We have had a happy and loving marriage. I have now learnt Spanish, which is my fourth language after English, German and French. It was nice to have my cousin Ena (Victoria Eugenie) in Spain. I didn't know her that well as a child, as she grew up in England and I grew up in Germany, but we got to know each other in Spain. Her mother is Aunt Beatrice, my father's sister, and she is also my godmother.

Spain did not join the First World War, so the war did not really affect me, unlike many of our relatives in the rest of Europe. My mother went to live in neutral Switzerland for the duration of the war but my sisters were on opposing sides. Missy in Romania and Ducky in Russia were on one side and Sandra in Germany on the other. However, in 1916 we also moved to Switzerland, as Alfonso was sent there on an official mission by the King. There were all sorts of rumours about why we were sent to Switzerland, including that I had undue influence on the Queen and that the King had made intimate advances towards me, which I had not returned. All I know is that he did not like me and wanted us out of the way. After spending some time there, we moved to England and our boys went to school at Winchester College.

Eight years later we were finally allowed to move back to Spain. However, in 1931 there were municipal elections and the republicans came to power in all the major cities, so the Spanish monarchy was overthrown. King Alfonso and Queen Victoria Eugenie went into exile, where they were finally able to separate. Alfonso went to Italy and Ena to Switzerland. We stayed in Spain for a while but when the Civil War began we decided to leave for England again. Our sons, who were adults by then, decided to stay in Spain. Obviously we lost our Spanish titles but I was still known as Princess Beatrice in England. We also lost our properties in Spain. Our son Alonso stayed on to fight on the side of the nationalists and he was killed in action, which was awful for us. After General Franco and the nationalists won the Civil War, we returned to Spain and have been living here ever since. As Spain did not enter the Second World War, it was a safe place to go. We have lived an unstable life and have moved around a lot. Although we have lost our titles and life has changed a lot, we have been living in Spain peacefully now for nearly 30 years.

Postscript: Beatrice died at their estate in Spain on 13 July 1966, aged 82. Her husband survived her by nine years. Ataulfo died unmarried in 1974. Alvaro had four children and died in 1997.

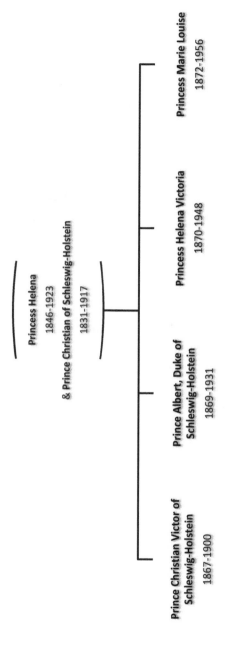

Family Tree of Princess Helena

Fifth Child of Queen Victoria

Princess Helena
1846-1923
& Prince Christian of Schleswig-Holstein
1831-1917

Prince Christian Victor of
Schleswig-Holstein
1867-1900

Prince Albert, Duke of
Schleswig-Holstein
1869-1931

Princess Helena Victoria
1870-1948

Princess Marie Louise
1872-1956

Princess Helena

Born 25 May 1846 – died 9 June 1923

I am the fifth child of Queen Victoria and Prince Albert. My father died when I was 15. When I was about 17, I had a relationship with Karl Roland, my father's former librarian and German tutor to my brother Bertie. We were together for a while but unfortunately my mother found out about the relationship and he was sent back to Germany, as he was deemed not suitable for me because he was not royal or even aristocratic.

Three years later, I married Prince Christian of Schleswig-Holstein. He was 15 years older than me. Initially, he was invited to England and I'm sure some people thought my mother was inspecting him as a possible suitor for herself rather than for me. Bertie and his wife Alix (Alexandra) refused at first to attend my wedding because Alix didn't approve of our marriage for political reasons, but fortunately my sister Alice intervened and convinced them to come. It was held at St George's Chapel, Windsor, on 5 July 1866. I was given away by my mother and Bertie. We stayed in England after the marriage, which was a condition my mother made when she gave consent to us marrying. We lived in our own residence in Cumberland Lodge, Windsor, but when we were in London we stayed at Buckingham Palace.

We had four children who grew to adulthood, although sadly I suffered a stillbirth and another son died when he was only eight days old. My eldest, Christian Victor, died of malaria during the Boer War in South Africa when he was only 33. Albert never married and my two daughters did not have any children. I didn't try and arrange marriages for my children. My youngest, Marie Louise, was married for a short while to Prince Aribert of Anhalt, a German Prince, but their marriage was annulled by his father. We're not quite sure why this happened but Marie Louise still considers herself married. She devoted herself to charity work after that. My other daughter, Helena Victoria, never married and also does a lot of charity work.

I also spent much of my time doing charity work, which was not common for royals at that time, but I have two passions in particular: needlework and nursing. I became the first president of the School of Art Needlework, which is now known as the Royal School of Needlework, and its objectives were not only to re-establish the art of needlework but also to provide a means of income for gentlewomen who did not have any other financial support. The idea was to teach them skills so that they could earn a living. I am no longer the president as my sister-in-law, Alix, took over when she became Queen Consort when Bertie (Edward VII) ascended the throne in 1901.

I was also the founding chair of the ladies committee of the British Red Cross and played a leading role in recruiting nurses and providing relief supplies during the Franco-Prussian War. I became president of the British Nurses Association on its foundation in 1887, which was initially set up to provide nursing care for soldiers but has now been extended to provide care to civilians. Nursing is a passion for me, as it was for my late sister, Alice. We were heavily influenced by Florence Nightingale. We saw her as an inspiration and we wanted to promote nursing in our respective countries. She greatly improved the role of nursing. I was also involved in providing 3,000 meals for children and unemployed men in the Windsor Guildhall during the harsh winter of 1886.

My relationship with my mother was a bit complicated. Although I loved her, she was often critical and we clashed over a few issues. One of them was women's rights, a cause I championed but she abhorred. She thought women should be looked after by their husbands. She was a very demanding and emotionally dependent person and did not always consider other's needs. She was used to having her way because she was Queen from such a young age, and was an only child before that.

I don't see much of my siblings these days. My eldest sister, Victoria, is long dead. Bertie and I were not very close and he has also died. His wife Alix was very hostile over my marriage to Christian due to a territorial dispute between Denmark and his family's territory of Schleswig-Holstein. She is a very difficult and jealous person and seems to hold on to grudges. I was closest to my brother Alfred. Even after he moved to Coburg, we continued to write to each other until he died in 1900. That was a hard year for me – I lost my favourite brother and my eldest son. My daughter's marriage was annulled that year. The following year my mother and my eldest sister died. I am the first of Queen Victoria's children to live into my seventies. My nephew, George V, is King now. I support him and represent him at official occasions.

My husband and I were devoted to each other but he sadly died a few years ago in 1917. He was 86. However, we did celebrate our golden wedding anniversary a year earlier. It was a little bit sombre because we were in the middle of the Great War, but nevertheless a happy occasion.

Postscript: Helena died on 9 June 1923, aged 77, and was buried in Windsor. She was addicted to opium, which she probably took to alleviate her health conditions, which included severe rheumatism and a lung condition.

Prince Christian Victor

of Schleswig-Holstein

Born 14 April 1867 – died 29 October 1900

I was born at Windsor Castle to Prince Christian of Schleswig-Holstein and Princess Helena, daughter of Queen Victoria. Although my father is a German Prince, we live in England and are members of the British Royal Family. I have three younger siblings: Albert, Helena Victoria and Marie Louise. We lived in Cumberland Lodge, an estate near Windsor. I was the first member of the British Royal Family to go to school, instead of being educated at home.

I went to Lambrook, a preparatory school in Berkshire, and then I attended Wellington College, which made Queen Victoria very happy as Prince Albert had established that school many years earlier. My brother also joined me at the school. I developed my love of cricket there and became captain of the cricket team. Then I studied at Magdalen College, University of Oxford, before joining the Royal Military College at Sandhurst. I was also captain of the cricket teams at Magdalen College and Sandhurst.

After I left Sandhurst, I became a British Army Officer and served in India and then Africa. I have reached the rank of Major and served under Lord Kitchener when we defeated the Dervishes in Sudan. Now I am currently fighting in the Boer War in South Africa against the Zulus.

Postscript: While serving in Pretoria, South Africa, Christian Victor contracted malaria in October 1900, which developed into typhoid fever. He died on 29 October 1900, aged 33, and was buried in Pretoria.

Prince Albert
Duke of Schleswig-Holstein
Born 26 February 1869 – died 27 April 1931

I was born at Frogmore House, Windsor, and my parents were Prince Christian of Schleswig-Holstein and Princess Helena. I had an older brother, Christian Victor, and two younger sisters, Helena Victoria and Marie Louise. I grew up at Cumberland Lodge in Windsor and like my older brother I attended Lambrook School and then Wellington College.

Like my brother, I also joined the Army but instead of the British Army like him, I joined the Prussian Army. I served in the Hessian Dragoon Guards and I reached the rank of Lieutenant-Colonel. I felt like I was following my father's German roots. However, during the Great War I was excused from active service by my cousin, Kaiser Wilhelm, as I did not want to fight against the British. I spent the war in Berlin as Governor. My brother, Christian Victor, had long since died in 1900 of malaria when fighting for the British in South Africa. My parents and sisters were still in England during the war, so we were separated during that period.

I never married but I did have an affair in 1900, from which we had a daughter, Valerie. I have never revealed the name of her mother because I wanted to protect her reputation, as she was of high noble birth. Valerie was placed in the care of a Jewish family, as neither of us were in a position to raise her ourselves. Now I am dying I have written to tell her that I am her real father. I have also told my sisters about her.

Postscript: Albert died less than two weeks later on 27 April 1931, aged 62. Valerie immediately changed her family name from her foster name of Schwalb to Schleswig-Holstein. In 1939, Valerie wished to marry for a second time but because of the Nuremburg laws she had to prove her ancestry, as Aryans were not allowed to marry Jews. Her aunts signed a statement officially acknowledging her, stating that Albert was her father, which then enabled her to marry Prince Engelbert-Charles, 10th Duke of Arenberg. Valerie died in Nice, France, in 1953 of an apparent suicide.

Princess Helena Victoria

Born 3 May 1870 – died 13 March 1948

My parents were Prince Christian of Schleswig-Holstein and Princess Helena. I spent most of my childhood at Cumberland Lodge in Windsor. My sister Marie Louise and I were educated at home and we had a very conventional royal childhood. It was only my brothers, Christian Victor and Albert, who went to school.

After we grew up, my sister and I would assist my mother and Aunt Beatrice with secretarial duties to Queen Victoria, my grandmother.

I have never married. At one point, I was a prospective bride for my cousin George (later George V) but his mother, Princess Alexandra, did not want us to marry because she had never got on with our family, as there has been a territorial dispute between Schleswig-Holstein (where my father came from) and Denmark (where Alexandra was from). She had also been against my parents' marriage, so she was not going to let her son marry me. In the end, he married Princess Mary of Teck and I was a bridesmaid at their wedding.

Another prospective husband, Ernest of Hohenlohe-Langenburg, married my cousin Sandra (Prince Alfred's daughter). Prince Johannes of Hohenlohe-Langenburg was suggested by Grandmamma (Queen Victoria) but he was Catholic, so that was never going to happen. I didn't have romantic

relationships with any of these men but they were all suggested to me as potential husbands.

In some ways I have had more independence as a single woman, even though I lived with my mother until her death and also with my sister Marie Louise after her marriage was annulled in 1900. I have spent my time doing charity work and carrying out royal representational duties. I have supported the work of the Young Men's Christian Association (YMCA) and Young Women's Christian Association (YWCA) as well as the Princess Christian Nursing Home at Windsor, which was a home my mother had set up. My sister and I are also enthusiastic patrons of music. I love watching tennis and I was often asked to present the prizes at the Wimbledon All England's Tennis Club.

When Christian Victor died during the Boer War in South Africa it was a loss which was hard to bear as he was still young. I travelled with my mother to South Africa to pay our respects at his grave.

During the First World War, I founded the Women's Auxiliary Force and as its president I visited British troops in France to try to keep their spirits up. My sister and I were responsible for arranging entertainments for them, which was fulfilling work. Obviously we didn't get to see my brother, Albert, during the war as he was living in Berlin.

In 1917, during the First World War, George V decided to change the German family name from Saxe-Coburg Gotha to Windsor to make the Royal Family sound less German and more British. Anyone with a German title was asked to relinquish it, so I became known simply as Princess Helena Victoria, as I dropped the territorial designation of Schleswig-Holstein.

My father died at the age of 86 in 1917 and my mother passed away in 1923, aged 77. After that, Marie and I lived in Schomberg House in London but it was damaged in the Blitz so we moved to Fitzmaurice Place in Berkeley Square.

Just before my brother Albert died, he told us that he had an illegitimate daughter named Valerie who had been adopted by a Jewish family. He would not tell us who her mother was, saying she was from high noble birth. It came as a complete surprise to us, as Albert had never married, although we had always wondered if any children had been born from any relationships he had. By then, Valerie was grown up but we did have some contact with her after he died. When she wanted to marry in 1938, she had to prove her ancestry because at that time in Nazi Germany the Nuremberg laws stated that Jews could not marry Aryans. Marie and I provided a statement to the authorities, officially acknowledging her and stating that Albert was her father, which allowed her to marry her fiancé.

My cousin's son, George VI, is on the throne now, so I have lived through five monarchs. We live in a very different world now to the one I was born into. I attended Princess Elizabeth's wedding (now the Queen) in 1947 and I feel that may well be my last public appearance.

Postscript: Helena Victoria died on 13 March 1948, aged 77, and was buried in Windsor.

Princess Marie Louise

Born 12 August 1872 – died 8 December 1956

I was born at Cumberland Lodge, Windsor, and was the fourth child of my parents Prince Christian of Schleswig-Holstein and Princess Helena. We were a close-knit family and my parents had a good relationship. I was especially close to my sister Thora (Helena Victoria) and we were educated at home but my brothers were sent to boarding school and we only saw them during the holidays.

In 1891 I married Prince Aribert of Anhalt when I was 19 and he was 25. We met at my cousin Victoria of Prussia's wedding in Berlin. I fell in love and we married in Windsor and then we went to live in Anhalt. However, we were unhappily married and spent quite a lot of time apart. We didn't have any children. I took any opportunity to travel to see my relatives in England and Germany. I also visited America and Canada and whilst in Canada in 1900 I received a telegram from my father-in-law summoning me to Anhalt. However, just as I was about to leave I received another telegram from my grandmother,

Queen Victoria, telling me to come back to England to see her. I decided to go to England and learnt that my marriage to Aribert had been annulled. Grandmamma wanted to spare me the humiliation of learning about this in Anhalt. Although we were unhappy, the annulment came as a shock. My father-in-law tried to blame me, saying that I had neglected my husband and made his life intolerable, but that was not true. It was actually because my husband engaged in scandalous behaviour with another man. Despite the annulment, I believe that my marriage vows to my husband are binding in the eyes of God, so I have never married again.

That same year, my eldest brother, Christian Victor, died during the Boer War in South Africa, so that was quite a bad year for me. After that I decided to live in England and moved back into the family home. I got involved in charity work, including the Girl Guides. I have helped to establish schemes to alleviate poverty and to provide ante-natal care for expectant mothers. I was also active in the Princess Christian Nursing Home, which my mother founded. I am also a patron of the arts, along with my sister Thora. I was involved in the creation of the Queen Mary's Dolls' House, which I gifted to her. My royal representational duties also kept me busy.

During the First World War, Thora and I organised entertainments for the troops at the Front. I also established hospitals and encouraged people to volunteer.

My parents and all my siblings are dead now. My father died in 1917, aged 86, and my mother died in 1923, aged 77.

I have lived through six different reigns and attended four coronations: Edward VII, George V, George VI and the current Queen. The Queen encouraged me to write my memoirs, which I did. They have just been published a few months ago, entitled "My memories of six reigns".

Postscript: Marie Louise died at her home in Berkeley Square, London, on 8 December 1956, aged 84. She was the last survivor of Princess Helena's branch of the family.

Family Tree of Princess Louise

Sixth Child of Queen Victoria

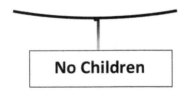

Princess Louise, Duchess of Argyll

1848 - 1939

John Campbell, 9th Duke of Argyll

1845 - 1914

No Children

Princess Louise
Duchess of Argyll

Born 18 March 1848 – died 3 December 1939

I am the sixth child of Queen Victoria and Prince Albert. After an unremarkable childhood, something amazing happened when I was 18: I fell in love with Robinson Duckworth, a rector who tutored my brother Leopold. Robinson was 14 years older than me and our secret relationship continued for about four years until my mother found out. She dismissed him from his duties and that was the end of our relationship.

It was then decided that I should be married off, which didn't prove to be that easy. My sister-in-law Alix (Alexandra) suggested her brother, the Crown Prince of Denmark, but my mother didn't want another Danish marriage in the family, probably due to her strained relationship with Alix. Victoria, my elder sister, proposed Prince Albert of Prussia. My mother didn't think that another Prussian Prince would be very popular in England. William, Prince of Orange, was also suggested but my mother turned that idea down too because of his extravagant and immoral lifestyle in Paris.

My mother wanted her younger daughters to live in England, so she was not terribly enthusiastic for me to marry a foreign prince if it meant living abroad. Eventually, since we could not find a suitable prince, I ended up being the first princess since Henry VIII's sister Mary to marry a non-royal. Mama over-ruled any opposition and I was finally allowed to marry

John Campbell, then the Marquess of Lorne. He became part of the family, but he did not have royal status. He succeeded his father to become the 9th Duke of Argyll in 1900.

We married in 1871 in Windsor, where most of my siblings got married. Windsor ensured that although it was a public affair, it was a little more private than marrying in London. Even my brother Bertie, who was heir to the throne, was married in Windsor.

After the wedding, we mainly lived in London and only visited Scotland occasionally. Initially we were in love but drifted apart and didn't have a particularly happy marriage, although we reconciled in our later years. I suspected him of having affairs and, shockingly, I think they were with other men. Unfortunately we were never able to have children.

John was involved in politics and sat in the House of Commons as a Liberal MP (as a non-royal he was able to stand for parliament). But after he became a Duke he had to relinquish his Commons seat and move to the House of Lords.

In 1878 John was appointed the Governor-General of Canada and we spent five years there. As the monarch's official representative in Canada, he opened the Canadian Parliament and did the things that the Queen would have done had she been in Canada. I loved it there but was homesick early on. 1878 was the year my sister Alice died, so that was tinged with sadness and that first Christmas there away from home was hard. We lived in the official residence in Ottawa, in Rideau Hall. It was far from the splendour of English royal residences but I fixed it up with our furnishings and put up some of my watercolours and oil paintings and my sculptures.

I found the cold winters a bit of a shock but I soon got used to them and my favourite pastimes were sleighing and ice-skating. In 1880 we had a particularly severe winter and we had a sleigh accident when the carriage we were travelling in overturned. It threw the coachman and footman from the sleigh and the horses panicked and dragged the carriage more than 400 yards. I was knocked unconscious when I hit my head on the iron bars that supported the roof and my husband was trapped underneath me. It was quite traumatic. I also injured my ear but we recovered.

We travelled around the country quite a bit and enjoyed visiting Quebec, where we had a summer home. I found the protocol in Canada a lot less rigid and my ladies-in-waiting were shocked by the more egalitarian culture. In Canada people from all walks of life were invited to attend functions at the Governor-General's residence, as long as they wore the correct attire. I ordered the removal of the silk cordon so that guests could mix together. Whilst in Canada my husband and I founded the Royal Canadian Academy of Arts. I was patron of the Ladies Educational Association of the Women's Protective Immigration Society, of the Society of Decorative Arts and of the Arts Association. I made a sculpture of my mother, which now stands outside the Royal Victoria College in Montreal.

I remember a particularly funny incident when we were visiting Bermuda. I was really thirsty, so I stopped at a house to ask for a drink. The woman who lived there was initially reluctant to help because she would have had to go to fetch some water and she also needed to finish her ironing. She said that she was rushing to do everything so that she could go and see Princess Louise later. I offered to do her ironing if she would get me the water, to which she agreed. She clearly didn't recognise me and I imagine that she would have been a bit embarrassed when she later realised who I was.

Back in London I spent my time doing a lot of sculpting, charity work, supporting my husband at social events and spending time with my mother, the Queen. Before I was married I served in a secretarial capacity to her. I loved my mother but I did find her difficult and demanding. Since I was a little girl I always loved art and then I gradually developed a love of sculpting and decided that was what I wanted to do. I convinced my mother to let me go to art school to train to be a sculptor. She was not very enthusiastic about that, as it was unusual for a princess, but I begged her and she finally relented. I couldn't attend full-time, as there were always other things to do, royal duties and so on. One of the sculptures I made is the statue of my mother, which now stands outside Kensington Palace.

I was a patron of the arts and of higher education. I was also a passionate supporter of the suffrage movement and even met Elizabeth Garrett, the first female doctor in the UK and supporter of the suffrage movement.

I didn't have a particularly good relationship with my sisters Helena and Beatrice. We were very different people, although our relationship has improved after our husbands died. I was closer to Bertie than my other siblings but after he became King I never invited him to visit my husband's ancestral home in Scotland because it would have been too expensive for us to host him. We used to have around 70 servants there but by the time he became King we were down to just four.

I have been accused by the press of having affairs, which is untrue. Of course it didn't help that Joseph Edgar Boehm died in his studio when I was visiting. He was a friend but nothing more. There were also rumours that I was having an affair with Lord Stanfordham, the Queen's Assistant Private Secretary. I denied these rumours and strongly suspected my sisters Beatrice and Helena had a lot to do with them. There were also rumours that I had affairs with other men too, but I deny them all – I just had a lot of male friends, is that a crime?

My husband died in 1914, when he was 68, from double pneumonia, so I have been a widow for around 25 years now. I took his death quite hard – I had a nervous breakdown and became quite lonely. We had reconciled by then and I nursed him before he died. I live in Kensington Palace now and occupy rooms next to my sister Beatrice. We are much closer now. I still make occasional public appearances but my health is deteriorating. I have always been very enthusiastic about keeping physically fit; I remember Bertie teasing me about it and I would reply saying that "I will outlive you all" and sadly this has become true.

I took part in my nephew George V's silver jubilee celebrations in 1935. Now my great-nephew, George VI, is on the throne and, of course, I have seen all the nasty business of my other great-nephew, Edward VIII, abdicating in 1936. My mother would have been appalled if she had seen that. I dread to think what she would have thought of Mrs Simpson, a woman twice divorced and for whom Edward gave up his throne.

Postscript: Louise died on 3 December 1939, aged 91, and was buried wearing her wedding veil. The Province of Alberta, Lake Louise and Mount Alberta were named after her.

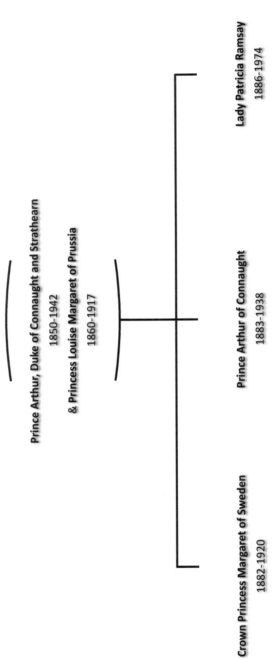

Family Tree of Prince Arthur

Seventh Child of Queen Victoria

Prince Arthur, Duke of Connaught and Strathearn
1850-1942

& Princess Louise Margaret of Prussia
1860-1917

Lady Patricia Ramsay
1886-1974

Prince Arthur of Connaught
1883-1938

Crown Princess Margaret of Sweden
1882-1920

Prince Arthur
Duke of Connaught and Strathearn
Born 1 May 1850 – died 16 January 1942

I am the seventh child of Queen Victoria and Prince Albert. I was 11 when my father died. I was educated at home by private tutors chosen by my father. When I was 16 I entered the Royal Military Academy in Woolwich and served in the Army until I retired. I rose to the rank of Field Marshall and travelled all over the world, including South Africa, India and Canada whilst in the Army and on royal duties. During World War One I was too old to fight but I still carried out representational duties motivating the troops and raising morale.

I married Princess Louise Margaret of Prussia, a minor royal, in 1879. I was 29 and she was 19, which was not an unusual age difference then. I was devoted to her despite my affairs. My brother Alfred and I were far more discreet than Bertie when it came to affairs. I think Louise did know about them but fortunately she turned a blind eye. We had three children – two girls and a boy – but I have outlived the two eldest children. We lived in Bagshot Park in Surrey, while Clarence House was our London residence.

I was appointed Governor-General of Canada from 1911 to 1916 by my nephew George V under the recommendation of Prime Minister Herbert Asquith. I was the only British prince ever to take that role. Although my sister Louise's husband had been Governor-General of Canada before me, he was not a prince. During the First World War I helped raise the morale of the troops and Louise volunteered with the Red Cross. I was given the title "Chief of the Six Nations" by the Iroquois people, who are native Canadians. It enabled me to sit on the tribes' councils. I enjoyed my time there and learned to ice-skate. Shortly after our return to England, Louise sadly died from influenza.

Three years later, in 1920, my eldest daughter Margaret died when she was only 38. That was a shock as she died on my 70th birthday. She had caught the measles and died of sepsis. It was very traumatic, as she was eight months' pregnant with her sixth child, and the baby died too. She was buried in her wedding dress with a crucifix in her hand. My only son, Arthur, died only a few years ago in 1938 of stomach cancer when he was 55. Only my youngest daughter, Patricia, survives but I do have seven grandchildren.

Now my great-nephew, George VI, is King and we are in the middle of another World War. I am living in Bagshot Park, which is hopefully far enough away from the bombs falling in London.

Postscript: Arthur died on 16 January 1942, aged 91, and was buried at Windsor.

Crown Princess Margaret
of Sweden

Born 15 January 1882 – died 1 May 1920

I am the eldest child of Prince Arthur, Duke of Connaught and Strathearn, and Princess Louise Margaret of Prussia. I was born in Bagshot Park, Surrey. I have a younger brother and sister, Arthur and Patricia. My childhood was conventional for a princess, being educated at home. I was known as Daisy to my family.

When I came of age, my family started thinking about who I should marry. Uncle Bertie (Edward VII) wanted my sister and me to marry a king, crown prince or someone in line to a throne. So in 1905, when I was 23, my parents, Patricia and I went to Portugal, where we were received by the Portuguese Royal Family, as it was hoped that one of us would marry one of King Carlos' sons, either Luis Filipe or his younger brother Manuel. We were entertained by the two Princes, whom we found very pleasant, but it did not lead to a romantic relationship. As it turned out, it was perhaps fortunate that neither of us married Luis Filipe, as he was shot dead along with his father, the King

by revolutionaries in the Lisbon Regicide of 1908. I could have been killed if I had been in the same carriage, or at the very least I would have been widowed.

We continued on with our trip to Egypt and Sudan but whilst in Cairo I met Prince Gustaf Adolf of Sweden. Gustaf had been considered as a possible match for Patricia but when we met we fell in love and he proposed during a dinner at the British Consulate. Patricia was happy for me, as she was not attracted to him romantically. We were married only six months later, on 15 June 1905, at St George's Chapel, Windsor. At that point, his grandfather was King but he became the Crown Prince in 1907, when his father succeeded the throne.

After the wedding we went to live in Sweden and I initially spent time learning Swedish and studying Swedish history. Sometimes I went out in public incognito so I could learn more about the Swedish people and how best I could serve them as their future Queen. I became involved in charities concerned with alleviating poverty. It took me a while to get used to Swedish culture and customs and to understand the different expectations of Swedish royalty. They are much more relaxed than the British royals. I don't think the people took to me at first because I was quite reserved because of my British upbringing, but over time I managed to become more relaxed in public and they seemed to accept me. I have learnt to ski and play tennis and golf too. I like art, particularly the works of Claude Monet, and also enjoy photography.

We have been very happily married and have five children. I spend as much time with them as I can, probably more than other royal mothers spend with their children. My husband really appreciates the environment I have created for our family, as he didn't enjoy a very close family atmosphere growing up. I accompany him on royal duties. We don't see much of my mother-in-law, as she is away a lot, so I have taken on quite a lot of her royal duties. My cousin Maud is Queen of Norway, so I see her quite often and also visit my family in England.

Sweden was not involved in the Great War but I created a sewing society to help support the Red Cross. I also helped to trace men who were missing in action. I had relatives fighting on both sides of the war and I became an intermediary for their letters, as they couldn't send them directly. As an English woman, I supported the British side but my mother-in-law was pro-German, which created some difficulties between us.

At the end of the war Sweden took some final steps towards democracy, which Gustaf and I supported, and this eased political tensions. In Germany my cousin Emperor Wilhelm II was deposed, so my mother-in-law, who was also his cousin, lost her political influence here. I find her to be very conservative, whereas I am much more liberal in my views.

Postscript: Margaret had measles, which she recovered from, but then developed further health problems, which led to sepsis whilst pregnant with her sixth child. She died on 1 May 1920, aged 38, along with her unborn baby, when she was eight months' pregnant. The Swedish Prime Minister declared that "the ray of sunshine at Stockholm Palace has gone out". Due to Margaret having a positive attitude towards reform, she eased political tensions and is said to have preserved the Swedish monarchy in the contemporary era.

Gustaf was devastated by her death; however in 1923 he visited London, where he met and fell in love with Lady Louise Mountbatten, Margaret's first cousin once removed. They were married and she moved to Sweden and became step-mother to Margaret's children.

Gustaf succeeded to the throne in 1950, aged 68, and died in 1973. Their eldest son, also named Gustaf, had already died in 1947 in a plane crash. Margaret's grandson Carl Gustaf then succeeded the throne in 1973, aged 27, and is the current King of Sweden. The law has been changed to allow the eldest child of either gender to succeed. The first in line to the throne is currently Carl Gustaf's daughter Victoria.

Prince Arthur
of Connaught

Born 13 January 1883 – died 12 September 1938

I was born at Windsor Castle and my parents were Prince Arthur, Duke of Connaught and Strathearn, and Princess Louise Margaret of Prussia. I grew up in Bagshot Park, Surrey, with my two sisters, Margaret and Patricia. My family called me 'Young Arthur' to distinguish me from my father.

I went to Eton College and then I joined the Royal Military College at Sandhurst. After graduating I joined the Army and fought in the Boer War, like my cousin Christian Victor, who died in South Africa. Later I served in the Great War as a Lieutenant-Colonel and after the war became an aide-de-camp to my cousin, George V.

When George V ascended the throne in 1910 his children were still young, so that meant my father and I were the most senior male members of the Royal Family and were therefore called upon to carry out public royal duties at home and abroad. On one occasion I went to Japan, where I met the Emperor, whom I bestowed the Order of the Garter on behalf of the King.

On 15 October 1913 I married Princess Alexandra, Duchess of Fife, my first cousin once removed and the grand-daughter of Edward VII. We had one son, Alastair, who was born the following year. Being away for most of the war I missed out a lot on his early years. After the war we lived in our residence in Mayfair. My mother died in 1917 from influenza and bronchitis and my sister Margaret sadly died three years later at the age of 38, when she was eight months' pregnant with her sixth child. However, I was glad when her husband Gustav married again, as Margaret would have been happy for him and their children needed a mother.

In 1920 I became Governor-General of South Africa for four years. After returning to England I became involved in a number of charities, including serving on the board of directors of Middlesex Hospital.

Postscript: Arthur died of stomach cancer on 12 September 1938, aged 55. His father died four years later, so Alastair succeeded his grandfather as Duke of Connaught. However, Alastair died the following year in Canada. At the time, it was reported that he had died from natural causes but it was later believed that he died from hypothermia after either having fallen out of a window or lying near an open window while inebriated. Arthur's wife, Alexandra, suffered from severe arthritis and other health problems and died in 1959.

Lady Patricia Ramsay

Born 17 March 1886 – died 12 January 1974

I was born at Buckingham Palace and my parents were Prince Arthur, Duke of Connaught and Strathearn, and Princess Louise Margaret of Prussia. At the time of my birth my title was Princess Patricia of Connaught. I was the third and youngest child in my family. I was educated at home with my sister, while my brother went to Eton College. I am known as Patsy to my family and friends.

We travelled quite a bit, as my father was in the Army. We lived in India for two years and in 1911 my father was appointed Governor-General of Canada, so I went with my parents and lived there for five years. We lived in the Governor-General's residence, Rideau Hall in Ottawa, but we also spent some time travelling around the country. I think I was quite popular there and they even named a Canadian Infantry Army regiment after me.

I had a number of prospective bridegrooms: in 1905 King Alfonso XIII of Spain visited England and my Uncle Bertie (Edward VII) was eager for me to marry him. We were set up together on formal occasions but I was not interested in marrying him and he later married my cousin Victoria Eugenie. That same year my sister Margaret and I visited Portugal, where we were entertained by the two Princes and it was hoped that one of us would marry one of them. In particular, it was hoped that one of us would marry the heir to the Portuguese throne, but in the end neither of us

did. Other suitors were also suggested for me, such as Prince Gustaf Adolf of Sweden, but my sister Margaret fell in love and married him in 1905. The Grand Duke of Mecklenburg-Strelitz and Grand Duke Michael of Russia were also mentioned, but I did not want to marry either of them, as I really wanted to marry for love.

Eventually I fell in love with Alexander Ramsay, a Navy Commander and a commoner. He was the son of an earl and we married in 1919 when I was 33, which, at that time, was considered quite old for a princess to marry. Fortunately by then it was no longer seen as an issue for a princess to marry a commoner. I chose to drop my title of Princess so we would be of equal rank. I became Lady Patricia Ramsay and he was Sir Alexander Ramsay. We had one son, Alexander, named after his father.

Sadly my sister Margaret died the following year when she was pregnant with her sixth child and my brother Arthur died in 1938 from stomach cancer.

My husband Alexander continued with his naval career. Even though I had relinquished my royal title, I was still a member of the Royal Family and I continued to attend royal events. In my spare time I enjoy painting watercolours. I have been inspired by my travels and have been influenced by Van Gogh and Gauguin's work.

My son Alexander served in the Second World War and lost his right leg during a tank battle in Tunisia, which was difficult, but I am just thankful that he escaped with his life. He was a favourite of my sister-in-law Alexandra, Arthur's wife, and as their son had died before her she left her estates to him. Alexander went to Cambridge and studied agriculture and he now manages the estates. He later married a Scottish noblewoman, Flora Fraser, daughter of the 20th Lord Saltoun. They have three daughters.

My husband Alexander died two years ago in 1972, aged 91.

Postscript: Patricia died at her home in Surrey on 12 January 1974, aged 87.

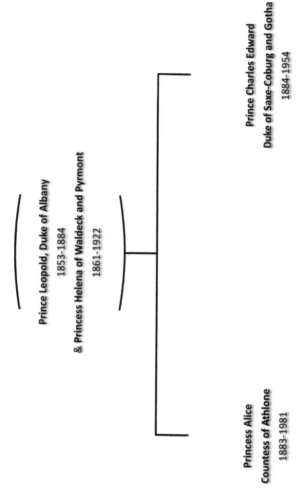

Family Tree of Prince Leopold

Eighth Child of Queen Victoria

Prince Leopold, Duke of Albany
1853-1884

& Princess Helena of Waldeck and Pyrmont
1861-1922

Prince Charles Edward
Duke of Saxe-Coburg and Gotha
1884-1954

Princess Alice
Countess of Athlone
1883-1981

Prince Leopold

Born 7 April 1853 – died 28 March 1884

I am the eighth child of Queen Victoria and Prince Albert. I was close to my siblings but I was not treated like the others because of my haemophilia. They found out I had the disease shortly after my second birthday. My parents were concerned about the bruises I was getting when I fell over, which were taking a long time to heal. They consulted doctors, including getting a specialist over from Germany, and he diagnosed me with haemophilia, which is a hereditary disease where the blood is abnormally slow to clot. It can be very painful – I get joint pain, which means that winters are hard for me as the cold makes it worse.

Spending time at Balmoral Castle can be hard because it is colder up there. I don't even have to fall over; even just stumbling can cause me to bleed internally. I have to rest and it can take weeks or months to recover. The disease can be life-threatening because you can bleed to death. Obviously this has affected my life. My parents were protective of me and didn't let me run

around or do sports, which made me feel very left out. It also meant I couldn't follow my brothers into the military, which is expected of princes.

I spent a lot of my childhood reading, while my brothers and sisters were being active. I did sometimes feel resentful towards my mother because she was so protective of me. It is a lifelong condition that can get worse as you get older. My sister Alice did not have haemophilia herself, as women do not seem to suffer from the disease, but passed it on to her son Frittie (Frederick), who sadly died when he was only two years old after falling out of a window. Although we knew this was something that could happen, his death was still a shock to us. I also have mild epilepsy too, where I appear to blank out.

As I didn't go into the military, I decided to pursue more intellectual subjects, like the sciences and literature. I persuaded my mother to let me study at Oxford University but unfortunately I wasn't able to complete an entire degree because my mother didn't want me gone too long. However, I enjoyed my time there and made many friends. After that I went travelling around Europe and then onto Canada and the USA with my sister Louise, whose husband was the Governor-General of Canada. When I got back I spent time serving as a patron of the arts and of literature and also as unofficial secretary to my mother. I didn't have an official role, which is not that unusual since I am the fourth son of the monarch. I served as an intermediary between my mother and various government ministers. My mother was never the same after my father died and lived in seclusion a lot of the time. My brother Bertie carried out representational duties, going out in public. We managed to persuade her to resume the state opening of Parliament.

I found it difficult to find a wife, most likely because of my haemophilia and epilepsy, which was a source of social stigma. I asked Alice Liddell, my friend from university, to marry me but she turned me down. Despite this, we remained friends. My mother probably wouldn't have allowed it anyway, even though her father was the Vice-Chancellor at Oxford University. I am godfather to Alice Liddell's son and she named him after me, and I later named my daughter after her and my sister Alice. It is said that Lewis Carroll based Alice from Alice in Wonderland on her.

I was desperate to get married because I saw it as a way to gain independence and get away from my controlling mother. In the end my mother helped me find a wife and introduced me to Princess Helena of Waldeck, who is very kind and unassuming. My mother likes her very much. We married when I was 28 and she was 21. She is very intelligent and likes solving mathematical problems and philosophy. I introduced her to all my friends from university. Before we were married her father had made her superintendent of the infant schools in the principality where they lived. She devised the curriculum, which was quite unusual for a woman to be given that responsibility. We are very happy together – we have a daughter, Alice, and Helena is pregnant again. I live in England but at the moment I am staying with friends in Cannes, France, because I find the cold English winters make my joint pain worse. Helena is staying at home because she is pregnant.

Postscript: Whilst in Cannes, Leopold stumbled and fell. He hit his knee and head. He died in the early hours of the following day as a result of massive internal bleeding. He wrote a last letter to his wife, writing until he ran out of strength, believing that he would probably die. The doctors were unable to help him. Leopold was only 30 when he died. His son Charles Edward was born posthumously. His wife never remarried but remained in England with her two children. She founded the Deptford Fund, which was set up to help women and girls in the cattle slaughter business to find alternative work. She was involved in several hospital charities and also worked to end human trafficking.

Princess Alice

Countess of Athlone

Born 25 February 1883 – died 3 January 1981

I was born at Windsor Castle and my parents were Prince Leopold, Duke of Albany, and Princess Helena of Waldeck. My father, who was a haemophiliac, died when I was only one year old. My younger brother, Charles Edward, was born after his death. We were raised by our mother and had a happy childhood. I was too young to remember my father but I do wish I had known him. We lived at Claremont House in Surrey and were still very much part of the British Royal Family.

I married Prince Alexander of Teck, the Princess of Wales' brother, on 10 February 1904. We had three children: May, Rupert and Maurice. Although I don't have haemophilia, both my sons had the disease. Maurice only lived for five months, which was incredibly sad. Rupert died in 1928 when he was 20 years old following a car crash. Had he not had haemophilia, he probably would have survived the crash, as his injuries did not seem that serious. I don't know what his life expectancy would have been, as haemophiliacs can die from the slightest knock,

but it was still very difficult to lose him. I only have May now and she has three children, who thankfully are all healthy. May married a commoner, Henry Able Smith.

My brother Charles Edward moved to Germany when he was 16 to become the Duke of Saxe-Coburg and Gotha following Uncle Alfred's death. We didn't see much of each other, particularly during the First and Second World Wars. He died back in 1954. I remained close to my mother until she died in 1922 following a heart attack when visiting Charles.

During the First World War, Alexander had to give up his German title, as George V wanted to make all the German relatives appear more British. We were then given the British titles of Earl and Countess of Athlone, although as I was a British princess in my own right, I also retained the title of Princess.

Alexander was a Brigadier-General in the Army during the First World War. He was appointed Governor-General of South Africa in 1924-1930 and Governor-General of Canada in 1940-1946. We lived in Rideau Hall in Ottawa and we took our grandchildren with us to keep them safe during the war. We spent a lot of time supporting the war effort. I carried out representational royal duties and also supported Alexander in his role. Alexander travelled across the country visiting the troops and hospitals. I was president of the nursing division of the St John's Ambulance Brigade. We also supported many charitable events and the arts. In our spare time, we learnt to ice-skate and had tobogganing parties.

We had many visitors who were fleeing from the war in Europe. Princess Juliana from the Netherlands (my first cousin once removed on my mother's side) and her family stayed with us for the duration of the war. Crown Princess Martha of Norway and her children, and Grand Duchess Charlotte of Luxembourg and her family also visited us for a short time. Winston Churchill stayed with us and presided over cabinet meetings from his sick bed. We also hosted the Quebec conferences, which were war-time conferences between Roosevelt, Churchill and the Canadian Prime Minister, Mackenzie King. I didn't get on with him but I found Roosevelt and Churchill quite charming.

After the war ended, Charles Edward was arrested in Germany by the Americans as he was a Nazi supporter. Alexander and I travelled to Germany to plead for his release but we were unsuccessful. He was accused of crimes against humanity; something I had great difficulty coming to terms with because of the love and affection I felt for him as my only sibling.

I have attended four coronations: Uncle Bertie (Edward VII), my cousin George V, George VI and the current Queen, as well as the investiture of the Dutch Queen Juliana, my first cousin once removed.

Alexander died in 1957, aged 82. I attended Princess Anne's wedding and the Queen's Silver Jubilee in 1977. I live in Kensington Palace and enjoy visiting the shops in Kensington and attending my local church. I feel privileged to have lived to see my great-grandchildren.

Postscript: Alice died in 1981, aged 97. At the time of her death, she was the last surviving grandchild of Queen Victoria and was the longest living princess. Her funeral was held at St George's Chapel, Windsor, and attended by all members of the Royal Family. She was buried next to her husband at the royal burial ground at Frogmore, Windsor.

Charles Edward
Duke of Saxe-Coburg and Gotha
Born 19 July 1884 – died 6 March 1954

I was born at Claremont House, Surrey, and at the time of my birth, I was known as Prince Charles Edward. My parents were Prince Leopold, Duke of Albany, and Princess Helena of Waldeck, but I never knew my father because he died just three months before I was born. I was brought up by my mother in Claremont House and I went to Eton College.

My early years were spent growing up as a British prince but in 1900 my Uncle Alfred, Duke of Saxe-Coburg and Gotha, died and I succeeded him when I was only 16. It had been agreed after Alfred's son died the preceding year that I would succeed him, but I didn't have much time to prepare. Uncle Arthur was actually next in line to the Ducal throne but Emperor Wilhelm II (my cousin) vetoed this idea as he did not want a member of the British Army to become a German duke. He asked Arthur to send his son to Germany to prepare him by having a German education but Arthur refused to do that, so then I was next in line. My mother lamented that after trying to raise me to be a

good Englishman I would become German after all her hard work. She was German herself but had adopted Britain as her home country when she married my father.

My mother and sister accompanied me there for a while before returning to England. For five years my cousin's husband Ernst was Regent, during which time I completed my education in Germany and joined the German Army. Wilhelm II was very involved in preparing me for my role as Duke and he became quite fond of me. I even became known as the Kaiser's seventh son. I spent some time at the German Court in Berlin. I was always loyal to Wilhelm. I assumed full constitutional powers as the Duke in 1905, when I was 21. At first I had quite liberal views but over time I became more conservative. I supported the arts, science and technology. That year I also married Princess Victoria Adelaide of Schleswig-Holstein, who was Wilhelm's wife's niece. We had five children: three sons and two daughters.

The First World War caused me to have a conflict of loyalty because I struggled with my conscience over which country to support, but I finally decided to support the German Empire. That meant that I had to break off relations with my English family, including my mother and sister for the duration of the war. At the beginning of the war I served in an infantry division fighting the Russians but in 1915 I had to stop due to my rheumatism. When the Russian Revolution happened in 1917, the world changed and I watched with much concern the struggles between left and right-wing parties in Germany. The following year the German Revolution occurred, which resulted in all the German monarchs being deposed. However, I stayed on in Germany as a private citizen since I was effectively exiled from Britain because of my involvement in the war.

I supported the Kapp Putsch in 1920 in an attempt to overthrow the Weimar Republic but unfortunately it failed due to the General Strike called in Berlin. In 1922 I met Hitler for the first time. In the presidential elections of 1932 I called on voters to support Hitler. I joined the Nazi Party a year later and I became a member of the Stormtroopers, the paramilitary wing of the Nazi Party. I also served as president of the German Red Cross in 1933-1945. My wife Victoria Adelaide supported the Nazis with me at first, but after they came to power she changed her mind and supported the German Evangelical Church, which was against the Nazis; her disobedience enraged me. My three sons also joined the Nazi Party. I visited Japan in 1934 to attend a conference on protecting civilians during war-time and also delivered Hitler's birthday greetings to the Emperor of Japan.

In 1936 I became a spy for Hitler when I attended my cousin George V's funeral. I also encouraged the new King, Edward VIII, to be pro-Nazi with the aim of creating a British-German pact. I sent Hitler reports about the pro-German feelings amongst the British aristocracy. Had Edward VIII not abdicated, maybe I would have been successful. I also hosted the Duke and

Duchess of Windsor (as Edward VIII and his wife had become known) when they visited Germany the following year. In 1940 I travelled to the USA to meet President Roosevelt on behalf of Hitler.

I was too old for active service during the Second World War but my three sons all served in the German Army. Sadly Hubertus was killed in 1943 in a plane crash. After the war ended I was arrested by the Americans and placed under house arrest because of my activities with the Nazi Party. My sister Alice and her husband came over to Germany to plead with the Americans for my release but she was not successful. I stood trial in a denazification court but was exonerated of complicity in war crimes. I was found to have been an important Nazi and was heavily fined by the court, which nearly bankrupted me. I also lost most of our properties because they were in the new East Germany and were confiscated by the Communists. Coburg was in West Germany but Gotha was in East Germany, where most of my properties were. I went with my wife to live in one of our remaining properties in Austria and have lived a very secluded life since then. We have been living in virtual poverty because of the fines I have had to pay.

One good thing that happened at the end of the war was that my daughter Sibylla, who was married to Prince Gustaf Adolf of Sweden, finally gave birth to a son in 1946 after having four daughters. He was third in line to the Swedish throne. Sadly for her, Gustaf was killed in a plane crash the following year, which means that my grandson is now the Crown Prince.

Postscript: Charles Edward died penniless of cancer in Coburg on 6 March 1954, aged 69. Victoria Adelaide outlived him and died in Austria in 1970. It is believed that Charles Edward could have been found guilty of crimes against humanity due to financing political murders, his knowledge of the death camps at Buchenwald and the euthanasia programme. However, because he was the grandfather of the future King of Sweden, it was decided that at the very least, if found guilty of such a crime, it would cause embarrassment for Sweden, or even possibly destabilise the country. The lesser sentence of being an important Nazi was handed down instead.

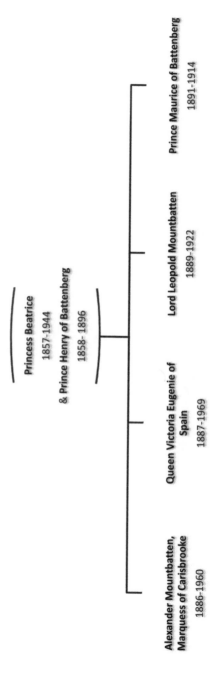

Family Tree of Princess Beatrice

Ninth Child of Queen Victoria

Princess Beatrice
1857-1944

& Prince Henry of Battenberg
1858- 1896

Alexander Mountbatten,
Marquess of Carisbrooke
1886-1960

Queen Victoria Eugenie of
Spain
1887-1969

Lord Leopold Mountbatten
1889-1922

Prince Maurice of Battenberg
1891-1914

Princess Beatrice

Born 14 April 1857 – died 26 October 1944

I am the ninth and youngest child of Queen Victoria and Prince Albert. My father sadly died when I was only four years old. I felt like I had missed out because my older siblings had more memories of him, whereas I could barely remember him. However, I grew up close to my mother. I was her main companion and she found solace in me after Papa's death. My mother could be a bit imperious, had a strong personality and was used to getting things her own way. But she could also be affectionate from time to time. After my father died, my mother became very reclusive, so we spent a lot of time at Windsor, Balmoral and Osborne House.

My eldest sister, Victoria, was 17 years older than me and she married and moved to Germany when I was very young, so I have no memories of her living with us. However, we were still close as we visited each other and corresponded by letter. I wasn't that close to Bertie because of the age difference and Alice was also living in Germany. I was probably closest to Leopold, but because of his haemophilia I didn't really have anyone to play with. I was educated at home, like my other siblings.

I shared secretarial duties to my mother with my sisters Helena and Louise. My mother didn't really want me to marry, as she wanted me to stay at home with her. I was also reluctant to get married, although I was attracted to Louis Napoleon, the Prince

Imperial of France, Napoleon III's son. I was fond of him but marriage with him was unlikely as my mother was against it and there was the whole question of religion, as he was a Catholic. She would definitely have opposed any marriage of her children to a Catholic. As it turned out, it was a good thing I didn't marry him because he was killed in action in the Boer Wars in 1897, aged just 23. I was happy to stay at home, as I only ever wanted to marry for love.

Finally, at 28, I married Prince Henry of Battenberg, one of my sister Alice's in-laws. He was from the morganatic branch of the family, which means that only one parent was royal, in his case his father, Prince Alexander of Hesse. Henry and I met at a family wedding in Darmstadt and we fell in love. I told my mother that we wanted to get married and she was initially so against the idea that she refused to talk to me for seven months. She would only communicate with me through written notes. Eventually, my elder sister Victoria convinced my mother to give permission for us to marry, but only on condition that we continued to live with her, which we did. It wasn't that she disapproved of Henry but rather that she was afraid of losing me. My husband accepted this, although he did occasionally get restless. He was a man of the outdoors. Eventually he wanted to see action, so he went to West Africa to fight in the Ashanti Wars and very sadly he contracted malaria and died. He was only 37 and we had only been married for about 10 years. I never really got over it and I dressed in black for the rest of my life, like my mother did when she was widowed, but I didn't seclude myself away like her. I never had any romantic relationships after Henry died.

My mother, on the other hand, had a couple of very close relationships after she was widowed. The first was with John Brown, one of her servants. He was very loyal to her and he seemed to bring her happiness. I didn't think it was as inappropriate as others said. It was purely a relationship of companionship, as my mother was very lonely after the death of my father. Later she was close to Abdul Karim, another servant. I didn't care for him at all because he became very prideful and he bullied some of the other Indian servants and generally lauded his position. I believe he took advantage of my mother in her old age and in the loneliness she was feeling, especially after my brother Leopold died. After my mother died in 1901, I spent time sorting through all her private documents as she had instructed me. This involved editing or destroying some papers and letters which she didn't want made public.

Henry and I had four children – Alexander, Victoria, Leopold and Maurice – who, like me, have had to grow up without a father. My mother was a doting grandmother to all her grandchildren, but especially to my children, as we lived with her. My son Leopold had haemophilia. He was named after my brother Leopold, who had already died from the condition, but it was a horrible coincidence that my son Leopold should also suffer from it. He sadly died in 1922, aged 32, during a hip operation. We knew that with his condition the hip operation was risky but that didn't make his death any easier. Like my brother, he had also led quite a restrictive life. My youngest son, Maurice, was killed in action during the First World War, which was terrible. Now we are in a Second World War, which seems to be going on forever.

I continue to carry out ceremonial duties, unveiling statues, that sort of thing. I live in Kensington Palace, not far from the rooms where Helena and Louise used to live. I was quite close to Helena. Louise was a strong personality and our relationship had its moments but we were quite close too.

Postscript: Beatrice died on 26 October 1944, aged 87, and was buried next to her husband on the Isle of Wight.

Alexander Mountbatten

Marquess of Carisbrooke

Born 23 November 1886 – died 23 February 1960

I was born at Windsor Castle to Prince Henry of Battenberg and Princess Beatrice, youngest daughter of Queen Victoria. At the time of my birth, I was known as Prince Alexander of Battenberg. I had two brothers and a sister. We grew up at the various British royal residences because we lived with my grandmother, Queen Victoria, as my mother was her companion. My father served in the British Army but when I was only 10 he died of malaria while on his way back to England from West Africa.

My brothers and I went to school at Wellington College. I didn't enjoy my school days much and had a hard time fitting in with the other boys. I found them all to be blood-thirsty hooligans. I was shy and quiet and didn't have many friends because I think they found me a bit stuck-up. I was not used to handling money and didn't know how to budget. I remember once I ran out of money and I wrote to Grandmamma (Queen Victoria) to ask her for more money, but she wrote back saying

I had to learn to look after myself. So I sold her letter to another boy, which helped me raise some money.

After school I attended the Britannia Royal Naval College and served on HMS Britannia from 1902 until 1908, when I transferred to the Army and served throughout the First World War.

In 1901 Grandmamma died. My siblings and I were very close to her, so it was a sad time for us and our lives changed considerably, as she had been such an important part of our lives, especially my mother's.

I have never felt drawn to women in a romantic way and indeed I had a relationship with Captain Hayes, an army doctor. However, I knew I was expected to get married, so in 1917 I married Lady Irene Denison, only daughter of the Earl of Londesborough. We were married at the Chapel Royal in St James' Palace and had a simple wedding because of the war. We lived at Kensington Palace and had a daughter, Iris. However, I probably did not make Irene very happy because for many years I have been in a long-term relationship with Simon Fleet, an antiques expert. Irene knew about him but she did not make our relationship public as she did not want to cause a scandal.

Also in 1917 my cousin, George V, changed the name of the Royal Family from Saxe-Coburg Gotha to Windsor, so we were required to drop our royal titles and changed our German name of Battenberg to the more English-sounding name of Mountbatten. At that time I was created Marquess of Carisbrooke and Irene became Lady Carisbrooke. However, this meant that I no longer received a state allowance, so as I needed an income I found work in the commercial sector. I certainly had not envisaged that I would ever need to find paid work and I believe I was the first member of the British Royal Family to do so.

I am very close to my sister, Victoria Eugenie (Ena, as we call her) who became Queen of Spain. I used to visit her in Spain when I was in the Army. I love to see her and I really love Spain. I particularly loved staying in the Alcazar in Seville, which I found really exotic, and the Royal Palace in Madrid was very luxurious.

During World War Two, despite being in my mid-fifties, I joined the RAF as a pilot until the end of the war. I was determined to do my patriotic duty and I was fortunate to survive both wars.

My mother Beatrice died in 1944, aged 87. She missed my father a lot after their 10-year marriage and mourned him deeply. Irene died four years ago. Iris has been considered by some as the "black sheep" of the Royal Family. After working as a nurse in the Second World War, she moved to the USA, where she has taught dance, became an actress and model and appeared as a hostess for a live TV programme. She has been married twice and her second marriage only lasted a few months. It was not the life I had imagined for her.

Postscript: Alexander died at his home in Kensington Palace in 1960, aged 73. He was the last surviving grandson of Queen Victoria (although Princess Alice, Countess of Athlone, the last surviving grand-daughter, died in 1981).

Queen Victoria Eugenie
of Spain

Born 24 October 1887 – died 5 April 1969

I was born at Balmoral Castle and my parents were Prince Henry of Battenberg and Princess Beatrice. At the time of my birth I was known as Princess Victoria Eugenie of Battenberg. I had three brothers: Alexander, Leopold and Maurice. I was brought up at the various British royal residencies, as my mother was companion and confidante to my grandmother (Queen Victoria) and so we moved around with her. My father died of malaria, which he caught when he was fighting in West Africa, when I was only nine. My mother was left with four children to look after, but unlike my brothers who went to school, I was educated at home.

My early childhood was fairly unremarkable but I do remember when I was seven I fell off my horse and suffered concussion. After my father died, I became closer with Gangan (the name I gave my grandmother), as she had also lost her father at a young age, so she understood what it was like to be without a father. We were very close to her as we lived with her, more so than some of her other grandchildren. Gangan died in 1901 when I was 14 and our lives changed a lot as my mother was no longer required to spend large amounts of time with her fulfilling her secretarial duties, so we moved into Kensington Palace.

In 1905 King Alfonso XIII of Spain came to England on a state visit and he swept me off my feet. I was only 18 and he was a year older than me. He had been King since the day he was born but had only starting reigning in his own right from the age of 16. After returning to Spain, we communicated by letters and our relationship developed. He asked his mother if he could marry me and she eventually gave her blessing after I agreed to become a Catholic. My mother and my Uncle Bertie (Edward VII) were very supportive of the match. We met up in Biarritz, France, for a chaperoned three-day romance. Later I visited San Sebastian, Spain, where I met my future mother-in-law. We went our separate ways and I was instructed in the Catholic faith and officially received into the Catholic Church in March 1906 in San Sebastian. A pre-nuptial agreement was signed, agreeing how much money I would receive at the start of the marriage and in the event of me being widowed.

We married on 31 May 1906 in Madrid. Some of my relatives, including my mother, brothers and the Prince and Princess of Wales, came to the wedding. However, when we were heading back to the Palace from the church, an assassination attempt was made on Alfonso and me. An anarchist threw a bomb at us. Fortunately, we were both fine but 24 people were killed and 100 were wounded. My wedding dress was splattered with the blood of one of the guards who was killed in front of us. It was a terrible start to our married life and completely ruined our day. I was initially calm but when we got back to the Palace I became hysterical for a time. Nowadays, there is a memorial outside the church to the victims of the attack.

I wasn't very popular in Spain. The people perceived me as being very different and were distrustful of me because of

Queen Victoria Eugenie with her children

my Protestant background. I had difficulty fitting into Spanish culture, as it was very different. I didn't like bull-fighting and I found it difficult to disguise my look of disgust when watching it, so I don't think that endeared me to the people. I spent the first year of my marriage learning Spanish and I gave birth to our first child, Alfonso, whom we named after his father. Everyone was initially very happy that we had a son and heir but we soon discovered that he had haemophilia. That was the beginning of my more serious worries. My relationship with Alfonso became very difficult after that because he blamed me for passing on haemophilia to our son, despite the fact that he had been warned before we married that my brother Leopold and various other members of my extended family had it and that our sons could inherit it.

Alfonso had many affairs and fathered many illegitimate

children, which upset me. I hadn't expected that he would do that because we had married for love. He even tried to seduce my cousin Beatrice. However, she rejected him and Alfonso had her and her husband exiled from Spain for a few years and I couldn't do anything to help her.

I had five more children and one stillbirth. Gonzalo, my youngest, also had haemophilia. Sadly, Alfonso distanced himself from the children. Our second son, Jaime, became deaf as a result of an operation when he was young. I have not had a happy life because of my difficult marriage, worries for my haemophiliac sons and being unpopular with the Spanish people. However, I was happy when my brothers came to visit me and I often visited my mother in England. Apart from bringing up my children, I spent my time working to improve healthcare in Spain by opening hospitals, encouraging women to become nurses and reorganising the Spanish Red Cross.

Although Spain did not enter the First World War, there was a very unpopular war in Morocco, which the Spanish fought to preserve our territory there. Spain won the war but at a high cost. There was a widespread perception among the people that Alfonso did not really care about his soldiers, which I think was true. I tried to help by sending nurses to help with the wounded. It didn't help that Alfonso had over-reached his position of constitutional monarch. During the war, he had encouraged one of his generals to continue with a battle, which resulted in one of the worst defeats of the war, the disaster at Annual. When he heard the news of the defeat, he simply shrugged his shoulders and returned to his game of golf. He was on holiday at the time and didn't return from France to comfort the families of those who had died.

In 1923 there was a military coup, in which a man named Miguel Primo de Rivera seized power and ruled as a military dictator with Alfonso's support. I heard a rumour that the Cortes (the Spanish parliament) had launched an investigation into the disaster at Annual, in which they would have inevitably discovered my husband's part in this affair and that one of my husband's reasons for supporting the dictatorship was in order to suppress this report. I cannot be sure if this is true or not.

In 1931, following municipal elections across Spain, the republicans came to power in every major city, so we were forced into exile. We went to France first and then to Italy and after that Alfonso and I decided to separate. I returned to England and moved back in with my mother. The final straw for our separation was when he accused me of infidelity, which was untrue and made me very angry; that I had always up until that point stood by him, despite him having many affairs, only for him to accuse me of infidelity.

The 1930s were a terrible decade for me after leaving Spain and the breakdown of my marriage. In 1933 my son Alfonso fell in love with a commoner and his father refused to let him marry her. He renounced his right of succession, even though Spain was a republic by then, and he went to live in the USA. I went to his wedding but his father refused to come. Then Gonzalo died when he was only 19 in 1934 in a car crash. His sister, Beatriz, was driving and swerved to avoid a cyclist and ended up hitting a wall. They should have taken him to hospital immediately. Some hours later, he was finally taken to hospital but they were unable to save him.

Four years later Alfonso also died as a result of a car crash, aged 31. Both accidents were very minor and anyone else would have survived, but they died because of their haemophilia. I had already lived through my brother Leopold dying from haemophilia during a hip operation when he was 32. I missed my other children so much that I moved back to Italy but still lived separately from Alfonso. I visited him just before he died in 1941. However, the Second World War was taking place and the Italian government accused me of spying for the British, so I had to leave Italy. I decided to settle in Switzerland, as I didn't want to make things awkward for my English relatives.

Jaime renounced his right to the succession because of his hearing disability. He married and had two sons, whom he named after his brothers, Alfonso and Gonzalo. Beatriz married an Italian nobleman and lives in Italy. Maria Cristina, my other daughter, also married an Italian aristocrat. Juan married and lives in Portugal. They all had children. Sadly, Juan's youngest son, Alfonso, was killed in a gun accident when he was only 14. No-one is quite sure how that happened but it is a terrible thing for a child to die like that and to outlive one's own grandchild.

In 1968 I was able to visit Spain again to become godmother at the baptism of my great-grandson, Felipe. It was touching to see the crowds who had come to see us. As former Queen, I could not stay in Spain for long, as General Franco is still in power.

Postscript: Victoria Eugenie died in Switzerland on 5 April 1969, aged 81. She had lived in exile for 38 years. She was initially buried in Switzerland but in 1985 her remains were returned to Spain and reinterred there with her husband. In 1975 the monarchy was restored following General Franco's death. He was succeeded by his chosen successor, King Juan Carlos, Victoria Eugenie's grandson. General Franco had passed over her son Juan in favour of Juan Carlos, who had been sent to Spain at an early age to be educated there with his brother. Victoria Eugenie's great grandson, Felipe VI, succeeded in 2014 following Juan Carlos' abdication.

Lord Leopold Mountbatten

Born 21 May 1889 – died 23 April 1922

I was born at Windsor Castle to Prince Henry of Battenberg and Princess Beatrice. At the time of my birth I was known as Prince Leopold of Battenberg. I have three siblings: Drino (Alexander), Ena (Victoria Eugenie) and my younger brother, Maurice.

We had a quiet upbringing living with my grandmother, Queen Victoria. My father died when I was only seven. I followed Drino to school at Wellington College. I have haemophilia, so I have to lead a quiet life, as any knocks or minor injuries can lead to death. So I was unable to take part in sports or even "play rough" with my brothers. My mother worries a lot about me as her brother Leopold, who was also a haemophiliac, died from the condition before I was born. I really wanted to join the Army, which I did, but it was in a non-combatant role, although I did serve throughout the Great War.

I have always been close to my siblings but Maurice was killed in action in 1914. My brother and I found his death very

hard. However, I like to visit Ena and her children in Spain. When she visits us, she usually comes without her children.

During the Great War, George V, my cousin, changed their family name from Saxe-Coburg Gotha to Windsor and he also wanted to slim down the size of the British Royal Family. Alexander and I lost our royal titles and I became known as Lord Leopold Mountbatten, an English version of the German-sounding Battenberg.

Postscript: Leopold died on 23 April 1922, aged 32, during a hip operation.

Prince Maurice
of Battenberg

Born 3 October 1891 – died 27 October 1914

I was born at Balmoral Castle and am the youngest child of Prince Henry of Battenberg and Princess Beatrice. I am the youngest grandchild of Queen Victoria. My early childhood was spent travelling between the royal residences, as my mother always accompanied her mother as her companion and confidante. My father died when I was only four. Ironically, my mother lost her father at the same age. Grandmamma's father had died when she was only one year old. People tell me that I look like my father. My grandmother died when I was ten and then we moved to Kensington Palace. We then led a quieter life as my mother was no longer needed as confidante to the Queen.

I went to school with my brothers and although my father died when I was so young, I had a happy childhood. After school, I joined the Army in the King's Royal Rifle Corps. It was always my dream to join the same regiment as my older cousin, Christian. I always looked up to him but sadly he died

from malaria when he was with the Army in South Africa when I was only nine.

When the Great War started, I was sent with my regiment to Ypres, Belgium, to fight.

Postscript: Maurice was killed in action at the beginning of the First World War on 27 October 1914 in Ypres, aged 23. Princess Beatrice insisted that he should be buried with his comrades. He is buried in the Ypres Town Commonwealth War Graves Commission Cemetery.

Addendum –
the royal line continues

Queen Victoria and Prince Albert had 87 great-grandchildren, and 142 great-great-grandchildren, including the current monarch, Queen Elizabeth II, and her husband Prince Philip.

Prince Philip, Duke of Edinburgh, born in 1921 and a descendant of Princess Alice, daughter of Queen Victoria, is currently the longest-lived, living great-great-grandchild of Queen Victoria.

Descendants of Queen Victoria who are current monarchs include Queen Elizabeth II, King Harald V of Norway, King Felipe VI of Spain, King Carl XVI Gustaf of Sweden and Queen Margrethe II of Denmark.

Photo Attributions

Alexander Mountbatten, 1st Marquis of Carisbrooke – Royal
  Photographers Bassano [Public domain]
Prince Albert, Duke of Schleswig-Holstein – Agence Rol [Public
  domain]
Prince Albert Victor, Duke of Clarence and Avondale – online
  [Public domain]
Empress Alexandra Feodorovna of Russia – Author unknown
  [Public domain]
Princess Alexandra of Saxe-Coburg and Gotha – Atelier Elvira,
  Munich [Public domain]
Prince Alfred, Duke of Saxe-Coburg and Gotha – Hawaii State
  Archives. Call Number: PP-71-5-012 [Public domain]
Prince Alfred, hereditary Prince of Saxe-Coburg and Gotha –
  Genealogy of the Royal Family of Great Britain [Public domain]
Princess Alice, Grand Duchess of Hesse and by Rhine – Carl
  Backofen [Public domain]
Princess Alice, Countess of Athlone – Author unknown [Public
  domain]

Prince Arthur, Duke of Connaught and Strathearn – Bain News Service, publisher [Public domain]

Prince Arthur of Connaught – The Library of Congress [Public domain]

Princess Beatrice – Author unknown [Public domain]

Princess Beatrice, Duchess of Galliera – B. Münchs Hofphotogr. Gotha [Public domain]

Princess Charlotte of Prussia, Duchess of Saxe-Meiningen – www.forum.alexanderpalace.org/ [Public domain]

Charles Edward, Duke of Saxe-Coburg and Gotha – Bundesarchiv, Bild 146-2007-0184 / CC-BY-SA 3.0 / CC BY-SA 3.0 DE (https://creativecommons.org/licenses/by-sa/3.0/de/deed.en)

Prince Christian Victor of Schleswig-Holstein – James Russell & Sons [Public domain]

King Edward VII – W. & D. Downey [Public domain]

Mother Elisabeth, Abbess of St Martha and Mary Convent, Moscow – nl:User:Broederhugo [Public domain]

Grand Duke Ernest Louis, Grand Duke of Hesse and by Rhine – Jacob Hilsdorf [Public domain]

Prince Friedrich of Hesse and by Rhine – Carl Backofen [Public domain]

King George V – W. & D. Downey (1829-1915) [Public domain]

Princess Helena – Hoffotograf [Public domain]

Princess Helena Victoria of Schleswig-Holstein – James Lafayette [Public domain]

Prince Henry of Prussia – Royal Collection [Public domain]

Princess Irene of Hesse and by Rhine – Author unknown [Public domain]

Lord Leopold Mountbatten – Hughes & Mullins: Ryde, Isle of Wight; Bain News Service, publisher. [Public domain]

Prince Leopold, Duke of Albany – Carl Rudolph Sohn [Public domain]

Princess Louise, Duchess of Argyll – Sergey Levitsky (1819-98) [Public domain]

Princess Louise, Duchess of Fife – https://carolathhabsburg. tumblr.com/page/23 [Public domain]

Crown Princess Margaret of Sweden – [Public domain]

Princess Margaret of Prussia and Prince Frederick Karl of Hesse – Unknown author [Public domain]

Princess Marie of Hesse and by Rhine – Author unknown [Public domain]

Queen Marie of Romania – George Grantham Bain [Public domain]

Princess Marie Louise of Schleswig-Holstein – James Lafayette [Public domain]

Queen Maud of Norway – Author unknown [Public domain]

Prince Maurice of Battenberg – Royal Photographers Bassano [Public domain]

Lady Patricia Ramsay -Illustrated London News [Public domain]

Prince Sigismund of Prussia – After Heinrich Graf, Berlin (1837-84) Additional creators: Cornelius Jabez Hughes (1819-84) [Public domain]

Queen Sophia of Greece – Royalty Digest; http://www.gogmsite. net/ [Public domain]

Princess Victoria, German Empress – Hills & Saunders [Public domain]

Queen Victoria Eugenie of Spain (and her children) – Unknown author [Public domain]

Princess Victoria of Hesse and by Rhine with her husband Prince Louis of Battenburg – Royal Collection Trust [Public domain]

Grand Duchess Victoria Feodorovna of Russia – Author unknown [Public domain]

Princess Viktoria of Prussia – L. Stüting & Sohn, Bonn.; Verlag v Wilh. Köhler, Bonn 2114. [Public domain]

Princess Victoria of the United Kingdom – Author unknown [Public domain]

Queen Victoria and her great grandson, Edward VIII (front cover) – iStock

Prince Waldemar of Prussia – The original uploader was Aldebaran69 at English Wikipedia. [Public domain]

Emperor Wilhelm II of Germany – Author unknown [Public domain]